2nd Edition

The Truth About Mold

Susan C. Cooper, BS, MS, PhD

Mike Buettner, CIAQM, CIE, CRMI
Contributing Editor

Dearborn™
Real Estate Education

This publication is designed to provide accurate and authoritative information in regard to the subject matter covered. It is sold with the understanding that the publisher is not engaged in rendering legal, accounting, medical, or other professional service. If legal advice or other expert assistance is required, the services of a competent professional person should be sought.

President: Mehul Patel
Vice President of Product Development & Publishing: Evan M. Butterfield
Editorial Director: Kate DeVivo
Development Editor: Tom Selley
Director of Production: Daniel Frey
Production Editor: Caitlin Ostrow
Production Artist: Virginia Byrne
Creative Director: Lucy Jenkins
Director of Product Management: Melissa Kleeman

Published by Dearborn™ Real Estate Education
30 South Wacker Drive
Chicago, IL 60606-7481
www.dearbornRE.com

Printed in the United States of America.

09 10   10 9 8 7 6 5 4 3 2

ISBN-13: 978-1-4277-7876-5
ISBN-10:   1-4277-7876-0

Chapter 5 — Inspection and Remediation 36

Chapter 6 — Policies, Standards, and Legislation 44

Chapter 7 — Reducing Liability 51

Appendix — Court Cases and Litigation 62

Susan C. Cooper, PhD, DTM, was originally trained as a scientist and has a master's degree and a PhD in physiology and biochemistry. Several years later, she received a second master's degree in geological engineering and spent 17 years as an environmental engineer at the Idaho Environmental and Engineering Laboratory; the Waste Isolation Pilot Plant in Carlsbad, New Mexico; and two environmental consulting firms in Albuquerque, New Mexico.

Dr. Cooper worked at the Albuquerque Metropolitan Board of REALTORS® (AMBR) for about five years, where she was the education/marketing coordinator and writer. While working for AMBR, she wrote many articles for consumers that appeared in *Albuquerque Homes Illustrated Magazine*, including several articles about mold—which led her to write this book. She was acknowledged as the "Mold Queen" after she and a REALTOR® in Albuquerque developed a course about mold for the New Mexico Real Estate Commission. They team-taught the course several times and presented the class at the September 2002 convention of the REALTORS®' Association of New Mexico (RANM).

Susan has retired, but she loves writing and has written a book about football (unpublished) and a number of articles for the art magazine *The Pastel Journal*. She also writes a column about local restaurants for *PrimeTime*, a monthly newspaper for seniors in Albuquerque.

I owe a great debt of gratitude to a number of people for their help and input with this book, particularly to Tom Selley, development editor at Dearborn, for all his help, and to Mike Buettner of Respircare Analytical for his contributions to and insightful review of the manuscript. Brett Engel and David Charlesworth of Acme Environmental answered a number of questions for me and provided me with a number of excellent photographs of mold for the original book.

This book would not have happened at all without Bill Hallett, who coauthored our mold course in New Mexico. Through the preparation of the course and teaching together, he has provided me with many invaluable insights into mold from the point of view of the real estate licensee.

Above all, I would like to thank my husband, Randy, for being so supportive throughout this process—and always. His patience and understanding played a large role in making it happen.

Introduction: What Is Mold?

learning objectives

After completing this chapter, you will be able to

- recognize the importance of mold and its function on earth;
- identify the names of the most common household molds (Group II); and
- identify the names of the molds often found in water-damaged homes (Group I).

■ Key Terms

ARMI	Group I molds	scientific name
ERMI	Group II molds	species
fungi	kingdom	

Mold has lived on earth for approximately four million years—far longer than we have been here! Until the sudden recent emergence of "toxic" mold in the media spotlight, household molds had not been considered a threat or a significant economic factor in our society. We all knew mold was around, but it appeared to be a harmless nuisance—household mold wasn't having any apparent impact on human health or the prices of goods or services, so nobody paid much attention to it. Common household mold wasn't perceived as a problem in the past, so little money has been spent to fund research on these organisms, and many areas of concern are still not understood. Now that mold issues are appearing in headlines on a regular basis, many people have developed a passion about mold. Because not very much information exists, much of the material published about molds is based upon opinions—and those opinions vary widely and sometimes conflict. Many of these diverse opinions relate to the effects that some molds appear to have on the health of certain individuals, but there are many other areas in which opinions conflict or in which no information is available at all.

The purpose of this book is to present the information currently available, which may change as more research is performed, and provide the reader with basic background information needed to understand the problem of mold—and so-called "toxic" mold. This book does *not* provide either legal or medical advice about mold and is not designed to turn real estate professionals into experts on mold.

Scientists categorize all living organisms into five major types of life groups, or **kingdoms**, primarily on the basis of cellular structure and method of feeding. Two of these five kingdoms consist of bacteria and one-celled organisms and are not relevant to this book. The other three are:

1. **Fungi** (fun'-ji, plural; fun'-gus, singular)—formerly thought to be plants
2. Animalia—animals
3. Plantae—plants

These three kingdoms—fungi, animals, and plants—are important classifications with which real estate professionals should be familiar.

Every organism within each of these three kingdoms is considered to be a *species*. A **species** is a type of organism with common characteristics. Members of a species can usually interbreed. The name of each species is referred to as its **scientific name**, which has two parts: the first name (in which the first letter is capitalized) is the name of the *genus*, which is more generic, whereas the second name (which is not capitalized) is the name of the *species*. For example, the scientific name of the domestic dog is *Canis familiaris* and that of the closely-related gray wolf is *Canis lupus*, whereas the more distant red fox is in a different genus, *Vulpes vulpes* (note that scientific names are always italicized).

■ Fungi and Molds

There are many different species of fungi, each with its own characteristics. Nobody has any idea how many species of fungi exist—estimates range from more than 100,000 to 1.5 million. Fungi are found everywhere and are essential for life on earth. Fungi—and molds—serve as nature's garbage disposal system. They break down dead plants and animals and their wastes. Without fungi, the earth would be so deeply buried in dead plants and animals and their excreta that there would be no room for us!

Species are grouped into categories within each kingdom. In the kingdom of fungi, the categories are mushrooms, puffballs, yeasts, certain kinds of plant parasites called *rusts* and *smuts,* and, of course, mold.

Just as nobody knows how many species of fungi exist, the number of species of *mold* is not known either. A conservative estimate is that there are over 20,000 different species of mold; other estimates suggest that there are more than 100,000. However, the actual number of species is not important: what *is* important is the fact that there are many species of mold, and that each species has its own characteristics.

This wide range of estimates of the number of species also indicates how much still needs to be learned about mold. There are a few important things about mold that we *do* know, however.

Molds may be found everywhere. In addition to their role in breaking down dead plants and animals, like other fungi, some molds are essential for the growth of many plants because they help the plant take in water and minerals from the soil.

Mold can be virtually any color: white, gray, brown, green, black, yellow, or even pink! Mold can look like cotton, velvet, or leather. It can look granular, like sugar or sand, or it can look slimy, like dirty oil from your car. Sometimes mold just makes a surface appear discolored or fuzzy.

A number of molds have commercial value. Some molds are used in cheeses like Roquefort, Gorgonzola, and Camembert.

Some molds are used in the pharmaceutical industry. Originally, the antibiotic penicillin was derived from a mold. A number of molds produce a chemical that is used to help prevent rejection of organ transplants. Other drugs derived from molds are used to treat high levels of cholesterol. Others are used to produce enzymes and organic acids (e.g., citric acid and gluconic acid) or to test soils or the effectiveness of various methods of preserving food.

■ Group I and Group II Molds

Although there are thousands of different species of molds, recent studies suggest that there are only about 36 indicator species that are typically found in homes throughout the United States. These 36 species are considered to be predictive of the relative moldiness of a home. Of these 36 species, ten species are commonly found in low concentrations in "normal" homes. They are referred to as **Group II molds** and are listed below:

1. *Acremonium strictum*
2. *Alternaria alternata*
3. *Aspergillus ustus*
4. *Cladosporium cladosporioides*, var. 1
5. *Cladosporium cladosporioides*, var. 2
6. *Cladosporium herbarum*
7. *Epicoccum nigrum*
8. *Mucor amphibiorum*
9. *Penicillium chrysogenum*
10. *Rhizopus stolonifer*

Because these are now considered to be Group II molds, it is obvious that there must also be Group I molds. Indeed, that is the case. **Group I molds are found** in water-damaged homes. There are 26 of these molds that may characterize "moldy" homes, and they are:

Aspergillus flavus	*Aureobasidium pullulans*	*Penicillium variabile*
Aspergillus fumigatus	*Chaetomium globosum*	*Scopulariopsis brevicaulis*
Aspergillus niger	*Cladosporium sphaerospermum*	*Scopulariopsis chartarum*
Aspergillus ochraceus	*Eurotium amstelodami*	*Stachybotrys chartarum*
Aspergillus penicillioides	*Paecilomyces variotii*	*Trichoderma viride*
Aspergillus restrictus	*Penicillium brevicompactum*	*Wallemia sebi*
Aspergillus sclerotiorum	*Penicillium corylophilum*	
Aspergillus sydowii	*Penicillium crustosum*	
Aspergillus unguis	*Penicillium purpurogenum*	
Aspergillus versicolor	*Penicillium spinulosum*	

■ The ERMI and the ARMI

ERMI and ARMI are two acronyms created by Stephen Vesper of the U.S. Environmental Protection Agency (EPA) and his colleagues. **ERMI** stands for Environmental Relative Moldiness Index, and it was developed to provide an objective standard to determine the moldiness of homes. A home with a high ERMI indicates a greater probability of a mold problem compared to a home with a low ERMI. This ranking system is often based on dust samples because spores accumulate in dust, dust samples are easy to collect, and the spores found in dust can be a good indicator of contamination problems in the home.

The ERMI comprises the 36 different species of mold listed previously. It includes the ten molds (Group II) that are common to many homes and the 26 molds (Group I) found in water-damaged homes.

ARMI is the acronym for the American Relative Moldiness Index. The ARMI was developed by the EPA as a more cost-effective analytical procedure than the ERMI because it requires the analysis of a smaller number of species of mold. Instead of the 36 molds in the ERMI, there are only 13 in the ARMI: ten from Group I and three from Group II. However, the ARMI is not used nearly as frequently as the ERMI.

■ Chapter One Review Questions

1. Mold is poorly understood because of
   a. lack of interest by the scientific community.
   b. our former lack of perception of mold as a health or industrial hazard.
   c. its complexity.
   d. its relative lack of impact upon our daily lives.

2. Mold is a member of the kingdom called
   a. Protista.
   b. Fungi.
   c. Animalia.
   d. Plantae.

3. Which statement is *FALSE*?
   a. Molds are vital because of their role in breaking down dead plants and animals and their wastes.
   b. Molds are always green or black.
   c. Molds play an important role in the drug and food industries.
   d. Molds are vital to the growth of a number of plants.

4. Mold is a type of
   a. mushroom.
   b. algae.
   c. plant.
   d. fungus.

5. The number of mold species known today is
   a. fewer than 100,000.
   b. more than 20,000.
   c. more than 1.5 million.
   d. unknown, but probably more than 100,000.

6. According to the ERMI, there are how many species of common household molds?
   a. Thousands
   b. Hundreds
   c. Ten
   d. More than 100,000

7. From the following list, which mold is *NOT* a common (Group II) household mold?
   a. *Aspergillus*
   b. *Penicillium*
   c. *Stachybotrys*
   d. *Mucor*

8. *Aspergillus ustus* is the scientific name of a mold found in many U.S. homes.
   a. True
   b. False

9. The *BEST* solution to the current mold problem is to exterminate all mold.
   a. True
   b. False

10. As established under the Environmental Relative Moldiness Index (ERMI), Group I molds are commonly found in low concentrations in homes throughout the United States, whereas Group II molds are found in greater concentrations in water-damaged homes.
    a. True
    b. False

What Does Mold Look Like, How Does It Reproduce, and When Does It Thrive?

learning objectives

After completing this chapter, you will be able to

- describe the structure of mold;

- explain the significance of mold spores;

- identify the three most important conditions that are needed for spores to be activated;

- identify food sources for common household mold; and

- list the most common sources of moisture that generally result in the growth of mold.

■ Key Terms

cellulose	hypha	starches
colonization	internal digestion	substrate
conidia	mycelium	sugars
dormant	sporangia	
external digestion	spores	

■ The Structure of Mold

Fungi are all simple organisms, and molds are no exception. The structure of the mold is called the **mycelium** (my-see'-li-um; plural: mycelia). Each mycelium consists of many interconnected, branched, tubular structures called *hyphae* (hi'-fee; singular: **hypha**). Specialized hyphae are formed for reproduction; they are discussed in the next section.

■ The Mold Life Cycle

Feeding

Molds have a unique way of feeding. In animals, food is taken into the body and travels to the stomach and intestine, where digestive enzymes are secreted to break large molecules into smaller molecules that can be utilized by the body. This is **internal digestion**. In molds, however, the hyphae secrete digestive enzymes *directly into the food source* to break it down into small molecules. Those small molecules are then drawn back from the food source, through the hyphae, and into the mycelium, where they are used as nutrients for the mold. This is **external digestion**. In other words, the digestive process in mold acts like an external stomach.

Reproduction

Like its structure, the life cycle of mold is simple: hyphae form, resulting in the development and growth of the mycelium. In addition, specialized hyphae develop that become asexual reproductive organs, since there are no male or female molds. Many species of mold form stalk-like hyphae that bear **conidia** (co-ni'di-a), spores that form externally on the side or end of the hyphae. Other species form hyphae that terminate in sac-like structures called **sporangia** (spo-ran'gee-a), or spore cases, in which the **spores** form. As each sporangium develops, spores form within it. The sporangium and its spores ripen, and the spores are released.

Spores are very small and light, generally ranging in size from 3 to 40 microns (the diameter of a human hair ranges from 100 to 150 microns). Many spores are released. In one experiment, it was estimated that a single puffball, another type of fungus, released seven trillion spores!

Because spores are so small and light, they can be dispersed in a variety of ways:

- After they have developed, they can be discharged by the mold.
- They can be picked up by a breeze or an air current in a building.
- They can be picked up inadvertently from contact with an insect, an animal, or a human being and carried away to another location on a purse, attaché case, skin, clothing, etc.

Once the spores are released, they float around for a while and ultimately land at a new location. Then they wait for ideal conditions (discussed in the next section) that will allow them to develop. When all those conditions are met, the spores germinate (like seeds), and the life cycle begins all over again, with the formation of a new mycelium, new specialized hyphae, and the development of more spores.

The advantage that spores give mold is that, regardless of what happens to the mycelium, the spores remain **dormant**, or inactive, until all essential conditions are met. Unlike the mycelium itself, which is relatively vulnerable and can be destroyed easily with a little water and detergent, a dormant spore can remain viable for many years. Spores are extremely resistant and can survive many adverse conditions that would kill the mycelium.

■ Conditions Needed to Activate Spores

Food Source (Substrate)

The primary food source of household molds is **cellulose**, which is a **starch** (a large, complex molecule composed of **sugars**). Because they need cellulose-containing materials to grow, nearly all the household molds that are currently of concern to the real estate world feed on organic, nonliving materials, such as dust and materials commonly used in the construction of buildings. Many building materials are made from plants such as trees, which are high in cellulose and therefore provide ideal feeding grounds. These materials include:

- Paper
- Cardboard
- Drywall
- Ceiling tile
- Wood
- Wallboard
- Carpeting
- Cellulosic insulation
- Wallpaper
- Fiberboard
- Natural fibers
- Paint

Sometimes it may appear that mold is growing on a **substrate** (food source) that shouldn't be supporting its growth, like concrete, plastic, or ceramic tile. In these instances, the mold may be living on a thin layer of substrate overlying other not-so-tasty materials and forming a *biofilm* over the noncellulosic material. Examples of common biofilms are molds growing on wallpaper, wallpaper paste, or even dust or dirt. Some water-based paints also contain cellulose and can support a biofilm of mold.

Moisture

The second major criterion for the activation of spores is the presence of moisture. This is by far the most critical requirement for mold growth and development since some kind of a food source is generally present. The amount of moisture and the duration of wet conditions required for activation vary according to the species of mold, but the presence of water in some form is absolutely critical for spores to be activated and begin to germinate. The presence of standing water and/or a relative humidity of at least 60 percent is enough to allow spores of most species to germinate. If the spores have a *continuing* source of moisture and food, an infestation of mold may develop.

Some areas in which mold often grows because of moist conditions are

- damp basements and crawl spaces,
- laundry rooms and bathrooms,

- garbage containers,
- water reservoirs for humidifiers,
- drip pans,
- unvented clothes dryers,
- humidifiers and air conditioners, and
- potting soil of overwatered house plants.

A number of conditions may trigger the presence or accumulation of moisture or standing water that leads to mold infestations. These include

- flooding, especially when the flooded areas are not dried out thoroughly or quickly;
- leaking pipes, especially when the pipes are hidden behind a wall, so that the owner of the home may have no idea that there is a leak;
- leaking windows and doors;
- condensation forming on or around a window sill or door or other areas;
- a leaking roof, if care is not taken to fix the roof and clean up the moisture;
- sewage backups; and
- toilet or tub overflows if frequent or if not cleaned up quickly.

Other factors can be poor housekeeping or pet urine. Any area with poor ventilation or insulation is at risk from potential mold infestations, especially if it is an area with high humidity or accumulation of moisture.

Naturally, mold problems can be much greater in regions with high relative humidity. Conditions often favor the germination and growth of mold in humid climates without a flooding or leaking event, and floods are harder to dry out because of the high humidity. For example, the new $95 million Kalia Tower of the Hilton Hawaiian Village in Waikiki was opened in May 2001; all 453 guest rooms were closed during the summer of 2002 because of a mold infestation.

Although mold is common in homes in Hawaii, fewer problems are experienced by people who leave their windows open to let fresh air in—and to let the mold out.

Can problems with mold arise in dry climates? Absolutely! Of course, problems with mold are usually not as extreme or intense in an arid region because everything dries out faster, and the average relative humidity is low. However, even in high mountain desert areas such as Albuquerque and Santa Fe in New Mexico, mold infestations can arise. In 2001, the Santa Fe public library was shut down because of a mold infestation. It reopened eight months and about $1.2 million later, after extensive cleanup that involved replacing the roof, air ducts, and some other structural components. A number of homes in Albuquerque and other areas in New Mexico have been ravaged by mold. A steady leak, if undetected or neglected, can result in an infestation even in such an arid environment.

In March 2002, a family in Rio Rancho, near Albuquerque, went on vacation. When they returned to their five-year-old home about ten days later, they found a most distressing situation in their kitchen: the ceiling had collapsed and was lying on the floor (Figure 2.1). Mold had taken over the kitchen. While the family had been on vacation, the line to their icemaker had broken, and their kitchen had flooded.

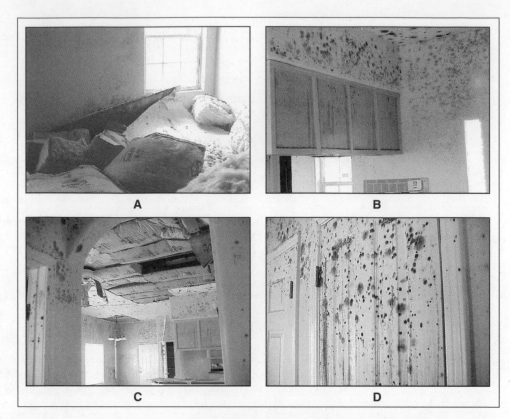

Figure 2.1 | a) Debris from the collapsed kitchen ceiling; b) Mold covering kitchen walls and ceilings; c) Exposed ceiling after collapse; d) Mold spreading throughout the house

Another example of a mold infestation in a dry climate comes from a foreclosure in Belen, a small town just south of Albuquerque. This home had been vacated for some time. Someone came in and stole the pressure tank (a tank used to store water from a water well and to ensure consistent water pressure) without capping it off. It is not known how long the house was flooded, but it was long enough for mold to take over the home (Figure 2.2). Bill Hallett, the REALTOR® who developed a course on mold with the author of this book, went out to take photographs. In order to enter the home, he had to sign a waiver at the Fannie Mae office stating that he would not hold Fannie Mae responsible if he became ill from the mold in the house.

Oxygen, Light, and Temperature

Mold spores require additional conditions to germinate and grow, but these conditions are not as crucial as the need for food and moisture. Most mold needs oxygen to grow, with the amount required varying among species, but some oxygen is nearly always available wherever and whenever spores are present.

Most mold grows well in dark places. It can often be found between internal walls, usually because of a leaking pipe.

Temperature is another minor factor. Mold has been known to grow within a wide range of temperatures—from 32°F up to 104°F. The acceptable temperature range

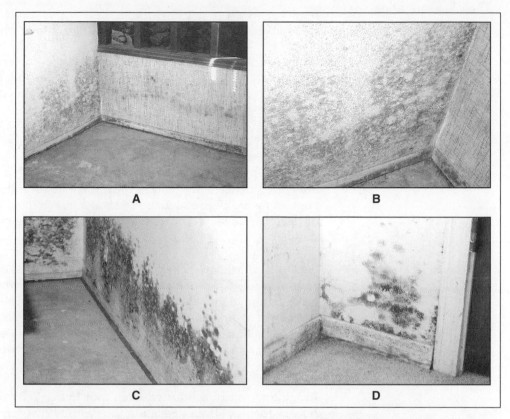

Figure 2.2 | a) Mold growth near the former location of the stolen pressure tank; b) A closer view of the corner of the wall near the stolen pressure tank; c) Mold infestation in the living room about 25 feet away from the stolen pressure tank; d) Mold in the hallway leading to the bedroom at the other end of the house

conducive to growth varies with the species of mold. If there is an ideal temperature for the germination and growth of mold, it is similar to *our* preferences—in the range from about 68°F to 86°F.

Time

There is one other critical condition required for the germination and growth of mold—time. When all other conditions are right, spores can germinate in as little as 4 to 12 hours. If the conditions remain good for mold, **colonization** of the mold—growth, maturation, and distribution of a new batch of spores—can take place in only 24 to 72 hours after germination, depending on the species of mold.

Here is an example of how quickly mold can gain a foothold and rapidly grow into a real infestation. One Saturday morning, a real estate agent was about to show a client a home, which had been vacated. She noticed water running out from underneath the front door and immediately tried to contact the owner to tell him that something had to be done right away. She called a plumber, who came out that afternoon and shut off the water to the house. She was finally able to contact the owner, who told her that he'd take care of the problem "right away." By Sunday afternoon, most of the water had drained out of the home, so the living room no longer looked like a large swimming pool. The owner finally sent an insurance agent out to look at the house on Monday. By the time somebody was finally allowed to get to work on cleaning up the water damage on Tuesday, a mold infestation had already set in. It doesn't take long!

As a rule of thumb, buildings that remain wet for at least 48 hours after a flooding event and/or a major hurricane will begin to show visible mold growth. If the buildings remain wet for longer periods of time, it is very likely that they will become infested with mold.

This is what happened in parts of New Orleans and other areas in Louisiana and Mississippi after Hurricane Katrina made landfall there on August 29, 2005. Thousands of homes were flooded under as much as 20 feet of water for weeks after the hurricane hit land, ensuring water saturation of all exposed cellulose-containing building materials. The water has drained from these homes, but many of the exposed surfaces are still moist, so they have become breeding grounds for molds.

Several studies have been conducted on the flooded areas of the city. In one study conducted in October and November of 2005, mold spores were analyzed at 23 outdoor and eight indoor locations across the city. The average outdoor spore concentration in flooded areas was approximately *double* that of non-flooded areas. The molds that were most commonly detected were several species of *Aspergillus*, *Penicillium*, and *Cladosporium*. *Stachybotrys* spores were detected in some indoor samples.

In another study conducted from November 2005 through January 2006, three houses that had been flooded in the Gentilly district of New Orleans were examined for spores and other fungal material. Huge numbers of spores were found, particularly the Group I molds *Aspergillus, Paecilomyces, Penicillium,* and *Stachybotrys*. The levels of mold detected in these homes were so high that they equaled or exceeded mold levels in wastewater treatment plants, cotton mills, and agricultural environments.

It should be noted that not all areas of New Orleans were flooded. For example, the French Quarter escaped flooding and emerged virtually unscathed.

■ Chapter Two Review Questions

1. To process food, fungi use
   a. internal digestion.
   b. external digestion.
   c. photosynthesis.
   d. internal combustion.

2. Spores remain dormant until they are exposed to the proper conditions for germination and growth. The three most important of these conditions are
   a. food, temperature, and oxygen.
   b. temperature, moisture, and oxygen.
   c. darkness, oxygen, and food.
   d. food, moisture, and time.

3. Which statement regarding common household molds is *FALSE*?
   a. They feed upon the cellulose produced by plants.
   b. They feed by secreting digestive enzymes into their food source and then absorbing the digested materials.
   c. They feed by internal digestion.
   d. They usually live on dead or nonliving organic materials.

4. Mold infestations are likely to form in all the following *EXCEPT*
   a. moist ceiling tile from a roof leak.
   b. the interior of a wall from a leaking pipe.
   c. overwatered house plants.
   d. wet copper tubing.

5. If the temperature of a home is kept at 65°F or less, mold will *NOT* be able to grow.
   a. True
   b. False

6. Some spores can germinate in as little as
   a. 1 week.
   b. 6 days.
   c. 24 hours.
   d. 10 minutes.

7. Mold problems can be reduced in humid climates by
   a. opening windows to allow for the exchange of air between the interior of the building and the outdoors.
   b. keeping windows securely closed to keep mold spores outside.
   c. running the humidifier more frequently.
   d. keeping the doors closed.

8. Which statement is *FALSE*?
   a. Mold is a very real problem in humid climates.
   b. Mold is less of a problem in dry climates, but infestations still occur in these areas.
   c. Flooding will not result in mold problems if the water is removed within a week.
   d. A mold infestation can result from something as simple as overwatered house plants.

9. Mold infestations should *NOT* occur in areas that are
   a. flooded but dried out within 24 to 48 hours.
   b. flooded but dried out within a week.
   c. dark, such as spaces between walls.
   d. behind a non-cellulose-containing material, such as ceramic tile.

10. Which of the following building materials does not contain cellulose and would *NOT* make a good food source for molds?
    a. Wallboard
    b. Carpeting
    c. Wood paneling
    d. Ceramic tile

Why Has Mold Become a Problem?

learning objectives

After completing this chapter, you will be able to

■ describe how energy-efficient building practices facilitate mold infestations;

■ explain how changing weather conditions and global warming may be contributing to mold problems; and

■ describe how poor design and/or defects in construction materials and methods may lead to mold infestations.

■ Key Terms

average surface temperature	global warming	PATH
	greenhouse gases	PD&R
exterior insulation and finish system (EIFS)	HUD	

Since mankind has coexisted with mold for so long, why has mold become such a problem and received so much notoriety recently? Is this something new? Or is it simply that our *awareness* has been escalated?

The growing concern with mold has been attributed to a number of factors:

■ Energy-efficient building practices

■ Poor design and/or construction defects

■ Changing weather patterns and global warming

■ Increased public awareness

■ Well-publicized court cases and legal activities involving mold

■ Energy-Efficient Building Practices

One of the reasons why mold problems have become evident is the increased use of more energy-efficient building practices, a change that was precipitated by the drastic rise in the price of oil and gas in the 1970s. New construction methods were developed to conserve energy. These practices, such as the use of double- or even triple-pane windows and caulking to prevent air leaks, keep warm air in and cold air out in the winter (and vice versa in the summer), but they also keep air—and moisture—trapped in homes and workplaces. This reduction in the exchange of interior air with outside air provides an environment that is conducive to the growth of mold. Lack of adequate ventilation also helps concentrate mold within buildings rather than releasing some of it to the outdoors.

■ Poor Design and/or Construction Defects

Partly because of changes in building practices, it is possible that there really *are* more mold infestations occurring now. Sometimes poor design and/or construction defects can also cause mold infestations. For example, a mold problem developed in a new 12-story addition to the military's Hale Koa Hotel in 1995, which is next door to the Hilton Hawaiian Village in Waikiki. According to John Jefferis, general manager of the hotel, the mold spores were tested, found to be nontoxic, and resulted in no health issues. However, the cost of remediation (cleanup) of the mold was $5.5 million. The mold problem was due to design and construction defects: the room dehumidifiers were underpowered and could not handle Hawaii's high humidity. Furthermore, a misplaced vapor retarder trapped moisture behind walls—a favorite breeding ground for molds.

Many people assume that mold is mostly a problem in older homes. That is not the case. Because of the tighter construction methods used in the building industry today, there is less ventilation, less exchange of air, between the inside and the outside of a home or other building so that any moisture—and mold—is trapped inside. Poor workmanship or construction defects, such as the failure to put in flashing around windows, may result in leaks and introduce additional problems.

Because these problems sometimes result in lawsuits, homebuilders and remodelers have become very aware of mold. At the International Builders' Show in 2002, mold was considered to be the biggest challenge facing the residential construction industry. Approximately 28 percent of the attendees at the show reported that they knew of mold in at least one home under construction in the past year, and 18 percent stated that they were aware of at least one occupied home in which there was a mold problem. They recommended that moisture be controlled during construction and after the house had been completed.

One reason why newer buildings are particularly susceptible to mold is that wallboard is often used for interior walls instead of plaster. Wallboard is formed by sandwiching a core of wet plaster between two sheets of heavy paper. Although the plaster itself is relatively impervious to mold since it consists primarily of lime, sand, and water, the paper backing of the wallboard provides an ideal environment for mold growth if it becomes wet. In older buildings, plaster, rather than wallboard, was generally used in the construction of interior walls, and plaster is not a good breeding ground for mold because it usually does not contain cellulose.

If a building is constructed at the bottom of a grade, water can collect around the foundation and will seep in through cracks. If a building is enclosed too soon after a heavy rain—that is, before the structural materials have dried out—the moisture from the rain will be trapped inside the building and may result in a mold infestation.

In one case, the owner of a new home built around 2001 in Albuquerque was plagued with continual leakage problems. He brought in a plumber, who discovered that all the piping used throughout the home in the original construction was defective and had to be replaced.

Lawsuits abound in the construction industry based on a variety of issues, including the following:

- Homeowners' and condominium associations are suing contractors for construction defects, inappropriate selection or installation of building materials resulting in mold, or breach of contract or warranty.
- Developers are being sued for excessive flooding of streets and yards, resulting in basement flooding and mold.
- Architects are being sued for defective design leading to mold.

The damages generally sought include compensation for bodily injury and health risks and to cover the cost of repair, remediation, or cleaning of discolored surfaces.

Another construction-related issue causing a number of lawsuits in recent years is *synthetic stucco,* a type of exterior siding and another name for an **exterior insulation and finish system (EIFS)**. If an EIFS is applied before the framing members are completely dry, moisture will be trapped inside and may result in a mold infestation. Considerable controversy exists as to whether the problem lies entirely in the manner of application, or whether the product itself is defective. Although some lawsuits have been reported in which the EIFS product itself was not found to be at fault, other lawsuits are still going on claiming a defective product. In fact, there are now companies that specialize in the removal of EIFSs. Many homes in Texas, North Carolina, and Georgia have had structural damage and had their value decreased because they are EIFS-clad homes. This appears to be an area of controversy that may remain unresolved for many years.

The Department of Housing and Urban Development (**HUD**) has been trying to help the construction industry avoid some of these mistakes through their Office of Policy Development and Research (**PD&R**). As part of the Partnership for Advancing Technology in Housing (**PATH**) Program, the PD&R has sponsored several projects that focus on key building practices and technologies to help prevent moisture problems, since moisture problems are the underlying cause of mold problems. The PD&R has sponsored the document *Durability by Design: A Guide for Residential Builders and Designers*, which is available as a PDF (portable document format) file. It provides a number of recommendations for managing moisture in and around a house and includes such topics as foundation drainage systems, roof overhang sizing, drainage plane design for wall systems, exhaust ventilation systems, bathroom design, and crawlspace ventilation. *Durability by Design* is available through several venues, including the HUD User Document Service at *www.huduser.org*.

Another publication available through the PATH program as a PDF is *Moisture-Resistant Homes: A Best Practice Guide and Plan Review Tool for Builders and Designers*.

This guide offers a number of best practices for managing moisture and was designed as a resource for builders, remodelers, designers, and homeowners. Like *Durability by Design*, it may be downloaded for free at the PATH Web site, *www.pathnet.org*.

Sometimes more restrictive requirements in building practices are triggered by a major catastrophic event. Because most of the homeowners who were evacuated from the area impacted by Hurricane Katrina in August 2005 are no longer making mortgage payments, the mortgage lenders are at financial risk unless the insurers of the homes or government agencies are going to pay for rebuilding or replacing the homes. As early as October 2005, many lenders were already requiring builders to use mold-resistant building materials and methods for preventing mold. In addition, homebuilders in southern Louisiana are now required to build to stricter standards so that new construction will be able to withstand flooding and winds of hurricane force (up to at least 110 miles per hour and up to 150 miles per hour in areas that are susceptible to high winds).

■ Changing Weather Patterns and Global Warming

Some experts claim that the increase in mold infestations is related to changing weather patterns, including excessive rain and frequent temperature swings, combined with a growing number of factors such as poorly constructed homes and tightly constructed, energy-efficient homes, all of which contribute to the moisture retention problem. This change in weather patterns has been attributed to **global warming** from the increase of **greenhouse gases** (such as carbon dioxide, methane, nitrous oxide, and fluorocarbons) released to the atmosphere from the burning of fossil fuels and other human activities. Only a few years ago, a report was issued indicating that the **average surface temperature** of the earth, a parameter sometimes used to estimate the extent of global warming, has increased by 0.5–1.0°F over the last 100 years. Later reports stated that average surface temperatures in 1998 and 2005 were already 1.28°F and 1.36°F higher than the average surface temperatures measured from the years 1950 through 1980, respectively. Furthermore, the years 2001 through 2005 were reported to be among the warmest years in recorded history. A paper presented in the prestigious journal *Science* indicated that there is a 90 percent probability that temperatures will rise by another 1.7 to 4.9°F by the year 2100.

The rise in air temperature has caused the sea level to rise 4 to 8 inches over the last 100 years and has increased worldwide precipitation over land by 1 percent. This phenomenon has also caused a decrease in the snow cover in the northern hemisphere and in the floating ice in the Arctic Ocean. In addition, the frequency of extreme rainfall events (such as El Niño) has increased throughout much of the world. This increased rainfall may result in more numerous flooding events and/or elevated humidity, both of which foster mold growth.

Higher sea surface temperatures have also been reported and can impact the frequency and intensity of such weather events as hurricanes. In October 2005, sea surface temperatures in the Gulf of Mexico were reported to have been higher in August 2005 than at any other time since 1890. Higher sea surface temperatures have also been reported in some areas of the Atlantic Ocean. Some scientists attribute these increases in sea surface temperature to the intensity of hurricanes

Katrina and Rita in 2005; however, whether or not the cause of the elevated sea temperatures and increased hurricane activity and intensity can be attributed to global warming is a hotly contested topic.

■ Increased Public Awareness

A major reason for the growing concern with mold is increased media attention focused predominantly on health issues. For example, many stories over the last few years have been published in newspapers and other media about mold problems in public buildings, alleging many of the health problems reported by employees working in the buildings to be linked to mold infestations.

In particular, many schools have had to be evacuated and closed in a number of cities and small communities throughout the country. In fact, mold in schools has become such a concern that the Environmental Protection Agency (EPA) has fact sheets on the topic and has made available an *Indoor Air Quality Tools for Schools* kit. Since 1999, the EPA has sponsored an annual *Indoor Air Quality Tools for Schools* national symposium that focuses on a number of indoor air quality problems of schools, including mold infestations. The National Clearinghouse for Educational Facilities (NCEF) has a Web page dedicated to mold in schools *(www.edfacilities .org/rl/mold.cfm).*

Hundreds of people who work in public buildings—county buildings, courthouses, libraries, office buildings, and even fire stations—have become ill with many of the symptoms often attributed to mold (see Chapter 4). Many of these buildings have been found to be infested with mold. Poor ventilation is often the problem. Office buildings in which large climate-control systems are used incorrectly, especially systems designed to recirculate air to conserve on air-conditioning bills, are particularly susceptible to mold infestations.

In one instance, Brett Engel of Acme Environmental in Albuquerque, an environmental mold specialist, was asked to look at a government building in which "too many" employees were getting sick on a regular basis (based on statistics). Mr. Engel looked at the building and immediately noted some signs of a potential problem. He observed that (1) the ground sloped in toward the building so that water would pool right next to or under the building, and (2) a stairwell had dark stains that looked like mold. Inside the building, he detected mold on one of the walls behind a door (Figure 3.1a). More mold was found in various places in the building, hidden behind filing cabinets and other heavy office furniture (Figure 3.1b). The cause was found to be an uncapped pipe in the basement of the building (Figure 3.1c).

Several members of ATC Associates (another environmental consulting firm) presented a mold workshop at the NAR conference in November 2002, during which they discussed a case involving a public building. One of the mold professionals from ATC had been called in to look at the building where employees had been getting sick. On one wall, he saw a stain that looked like a narrow squiggly line running across the wall, which was a little larger and more intense toward the middle of the wall. "There's your problem," he told the manager of the building who had asked him for his services. "We need to cut a hole in the wall with the stain to see what's on the other side." The manager of the building said that the stain had been there for years and that he wasn't about to have any holes cut in the wall. Several weeks later, he called the specialist back and authorized him to

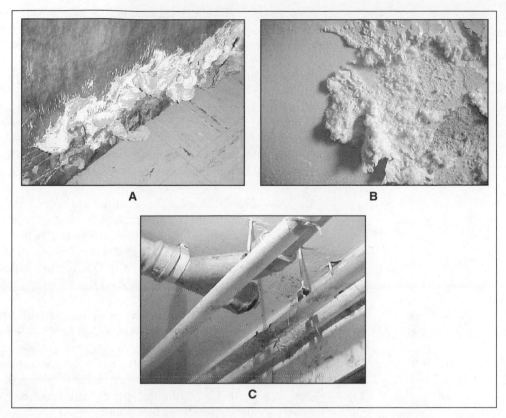

Figure 3.1 | a) Mold on the wall of a government building; b) Large mold growth found behind a filing cabinet; c) Cause of the mold infestation: an uncapped pipe

examine the wall behind the stain. It was covered with mold. The problem was found to be a pinhole leak in a pipe. Every time the pipe was under pressure, water was released.

■ Well-Publicized Court Cases and Legal Activities Involving Mold

One of the major reasons why mold has become such an issue has been all the court cases filed (see the appendix for examples). Many of these court cases have resulted in heavy fines and penalties against real estate professionals, including agents, brokers, and property managers. However, the homeowners' insurance industry has been most adversely impacted.

A number of mold-related lawsuits have been filed against the providers of homeowners' insurance. The most notorious of these was the case in which Melinda Ballard and her family, who lived in a mansion in Dripping Springs, Texas, sued her insurance company. The court awarded her $32 million. (An appeals court later reduced the amount of the award to approximately $8.5 million.)

The Ballard case triggered the onset of many other mold-related claims and lawsuits. At one time during the early years of the 21st century, over 10,000 lawsuits alleging mold contamination in homes were active; many of these claims and lawsuits were in Texas. During the first quarter of 2000, only about 1,000 mold-related insurance claims were reported in the state. By the fourth quarter of 2001, the number of claims filed had soared to over 14,000, while the size of the average claim filed in Texas grew from $500 to $15,000. In Texas alone, 227,000 claims were filed in 2002, costing insurers $2.2 billion, at an average cost of about $30,000 per claim, compared with most other homeowner claims, which usually cost about $3,000 to 4,000 per claim. So, between the lawsuits and the excessive claims, the major providers of homeowners' insurance in Texas were hurt so badly that they stopped writing homeowners' insurance policies in the state for a while.

The problem has not been restricted to Texas. Many other states have been directly impacted, as well, particularly California and Florida.

It is very likely that an unprecedented number of mold-related claims and lawsuits will come from the states hit hardest by Hurricane Katrina. As early as October 26, 2005, less than two months after Hurricane Katrina made landfall, preliminary damage estimates suggested that Katrina had already become "the most costly insured loss from a single event in U.S. history" (Robertson, 2005), even more so than Hurricane Andrew in 1992 and the terrorist attacks on September 11, 2001.

After Hurricane Katrina and the subsequent flooding events from the failure of the levees in New Orleans, more than 40,000 homes were buried under 20 feet of water for weeks—and that was in only one parish (St. Bernard's Parish). When the water had drained off the houses that had flooded, water-saturated cellulose-containing materials were left exposed everywhere. The weather was hot and humid. Altogether, a perfect breeding ground for mold had been created. In many buildings, nearly every exposed surface was covered with mold. Many of these buildings, although left relatively intact by the storm itself, will have to be razed because of the ravages of the mold infestations.

The first wave of lawsuits filed (647 of them) hit the courts by August 29, 2006, the date of the original one-year deadline for filing lawsuits subsequent to the Katrina disaster. Although a newly enacted law gave homeowners until the fall of 2007 to file, the constitutionality of the extension had not been validated until the state Supreme Court finally ruled on it on August 25, 2006.

Most of these early lawsuits, which are just the beginning of the court cases that can be anticipated, have been filed between individuals or businesses and their insurance companies. There will undoubtedly be many more, not only by the owners of the houses destroyed by mold, but also by unskilled workers who helped with the initial cleanup activities without proper training or personal protective equipment and were thus exposed not only to mold, but to other hazardous materials, such as oil, gas, chemicals, *Escherichia coli*, other bacteria, lead, and arsenic in the flood waters. There will be claims because of construction defects and mold pre-dating Katrina that were not discovered until afterwards, and there will be claims from people returning to their homes and getting sick from mold that may still be hidden behind walls, in air ducts, in carpets—the list goes on and on.

History is already repeating itself regarding insurance issues. In January 2007, a U.S. District Judge ruled against State Farm Fire and Casualty Company in a Katrina-related damage claim by a property owner. Norman and Genevieve Broussard lost their home in Biloxi, Mississippi, when a tornado caused by Katrina slammed into it, destroying the home and leaving only a concrete slab. State Farm refused to pay the claim because they stated that the home had been destroyed by Katrina's storm surge and that the Broussard's policy did not cover water damage. Broussard's attorneys accused State Farm of breach of contract. The judge has ordered State Farm to pay $232,292 in damages; the plaintiffs are also seeking $5 million in punitive damages. Because of that defeat, State Farm stated in February 2007 that it will no longer insure homeowners or businesses in Mississippi. State Farm has been the largest single insurer in Mississippi, with a 30 percent market share. (In 2006, Allstate refused to issue property insurance for Mississippi's six coastal counties.) In retaliation, the Attorney General of Mississippi is planning to file a civil suit against State Farm over the company's refusal to pay some of the claims from 2005.

As of February 2006, claims and lawsuits resulting from hurricanes Katrina, Rita, and Wilma (major hurricanes that hit in 2005) are estimated to have cost insurance companies nearly $58 billion. According to a report issued by the Risk and Insurance Management Society, property insurance rates increased substantially during the fourth quarter of 2006, in some cases by as much as 33 percent because this amount was more than could be absorbed by the insurance companies.

Because of the earlier lawsuits and claims in Texas, homeowners' insurance providers had already modified some of the methods they use for accepting new clients, and it has become increasingly difficult for homeowners to obtain insurance. Mold damage is now specifically excluded from coverage in most policies for homes and commercial properties. It may or may not be covered under these policies if the mold damage results from a "covered peril," such as a broken pipe. Mold damage from flooding is generally covered only under flood insurance available through the National Flood Insurance Program (NFIP), but each issue is evaluated on a case-by-case basis.

Homeowners' insurance has become a nightmare to many professionals in the real estate industry. Generally, insurance companies will not sell policies to any buyer wanting to purchase a home for which water damage and/or mold claims had been filed by the seller of the home. Some companies are not selling policies to a buyer if *any* claims had been filed on the home within the last three to five years. Furthermore, if someone who holds a homeowners' insurance policy calls his or her agent to ask for information (such as the size of the deductible on their policy), that phone call may appear as a claim!

It is nearly always possible for a new homeowner to find insurance on a home, even if denied insurance by one of the major providers. However, the insurance policy that the new homeowner *can* find is sometimes so expensive that he or she cannot afford it—and it may kill the sale. Furthermore, the policy usually provides minimal protection for the homebuyer. (See also Chapter 7.)

■ Chapter Three Review Questions

1. One of the reasons for the increase in mold-related problems recently is
   a. the increased "tightness" of homes built since the 1970s.
   b. too much ventilation being used in homes, allowing mold to come inside homes from outdoors.
   c. the plaster used in building older homes.
   d. the development of mutations that make molds more resistant.

2. The mold problem reported in the new Hale Koa Hotel in Hawaii was attributed to defective materials used in its construction.
   a. True
   b. False

3. Which statement is *TRUE*?
   a. Buildings in arid climates are not subject to major mold infestations.
   b. Only older homes have mold problems.
   c. New homes rarely have mold infestations.
   d. Any building is susceptible to mold problems if it has a continuing moisture problem.

4. Older homes are particularly susceptible to mold because of the plaster frequently used in their construction.
   a. True
   b. False

5. The rise in the average surface temperature of the Earth over the last 100 years is reported to have caused a rise in sea level of
   a. 8 to 12 inches and a 1 percent increase in worldwide precipitation.
   b. 4 to 8 inches and a 10 percent increase in worldwide precipitation.
   c. 8 to 12 inches and a 10 percent increase in worldwide precipitation.
   d. 4 to 8 inches and a 1 percent increase in worldwide precipitation.

6. The increased frequency and intensity of major weather events, like hurricanes, has been attributed to global warming by some scientists.
   a. True
   b. False

7. The concerns of the CDC and the EPA have been instrumental in publicizing mold problems.
   a. True
   b. False

8. A well-ventilated home is often more subject to mold infestations than is a "tight" home.
   a. True
   b. False

9. Mold infestations are restricted to buildings in high-humidity climates.
   a. True
   b. False

10. Builders and remodelers have *NOT* yet been impacted by mold problems.
    a. True
    b. False

Adverse Health Effects of Mold

learning objectives

After completing this chapter, you will be able to

■ identify the three major types of illness that can be caused by common household molds;

■ describe mycotoxins and recognize which molds produce them, under what conditions, and why;

■ identify the adverse health effects that have been known and alleged to be caused by mycotoxins; and

■ explain why illness caused by mold is challenging for physicians to diagnose.

■ Key Terms

allergen	hypersensitive	opportunistic pathogen
allergy	hypersensitivity	parasite
antigen	pneumonitis	saprophyte
antibody	immune system	sensitization
aspergillosis	infection	sinusitis
biomarkers	invasive aspergillosis	*Stachybotrys chartarum*
Fusarium	mycotoxin	volatile organic
glucans	obstructive lung disease	compounds (VOCs)

One of the challenges with molds and their health effects upon humans is that those effects are so unpredictable. Anyone who has ever hunted knows that it is much harder to hit a moving target than a stationary one. The difficulty of hitting the target is compounded if the target moves randomly rather than in a predictable

IMPORTANT: No information put forth in this text should be construed as an attempt to provide medical advice. Please consult a physician with any questions or concerns you may have regarding your health and mold in your home or business.

fashion. A target that moves randomly is similar to the effect of mold upon human health because individual responses vary so much—it is, indeed, much like a target that moves at random.

■ Mold and the Immune System

Human responses to mold are determined by a variety of factors, including the individual's physical condition, age, degree of exposure, sensitivity to mold, and susceptibility to disease.

The **immune system** is our primary defense mechanism against foreign materials invading our bodies. These foreign materials are referred to as **antigens**; they can be anything entering our bodies that doesn't belong there, including viruses, bacteria, and fungi. These antigens can gain access through our skin (through a cut or, if the antigen is fat soluble, through the skin itself), by ingestion, or by breathing in the material. Antigens are often bacteria or viruses, but they may also be pollen, dust, or any other small material, such as mold (generally in the form of spores or fragments of mycelia).

Antigens frequently enter our bodies—they are part of living. If we and our immune systems are healthy, the introduction of most antigens usually causes no problem: the antigens stimulate the production of **antibodies** by our white blood cells. These antibodies engulf or neutralize the antigens and effectively remove them from our bodies.

People who are particularly vulnerable to molds are often suffering from allergies, asthma, or a compromised or weakened immune system. The following types of individuals are particularly at risk:

- Infants and small children are vulnerable because their immune systems are not yet fully developed.
- Elderly people become susceptible when their immune systems weaken with age.
- Those who are ill, recovering from surgery, suffering from an HIV-positive status or AIDS, or undergoing chemotherapy generally have depressed immune systems. This is also true of people who suffer from asthma, multiple allergies, or other respiratory problems.

Conversely, individuals with a strong immune system will be less susceptible to mold. However, even a person with a typically strong immune system will have bad days because of illness, lack of sleep, stress, or even too much partying. On those days, that person will be more susceptible to mold than usual.

Sometimes people become *sensitized* to mold, which increases their vulnerability. **Sensitization** to mold requires repeated exposure to the mold **allergen** (an antigen that causes an allergic reaction). As a result, the individual becomes hypersensitive to that material. For example, farmers often work around moldy hay. After years of repeated exposure to the mold in the hay, they may become hypersensitive to the mold and may even have to hire someone else to work in those areas—or get out of the farming business entirely. Even office workers who work in mold-infested buildings and were not previously allergic to molds can become **hypersensitive** with repeated exposure to the mold in the workplace.

■ Health Effects of Mold

All molds produce chemicals, and those chemicals vary with the mold and the conditions to which the mold is exposed. The fact that each chemical causes a different response increases the variability of individual responses to mold.

Exposure to molds generally results in one of three different types of responses:

1. Irritations
2. Allergies
3. Infections

Irritations Caused by Molds

Irritations from molds are often caused by their production of waste products known as **volatile organic compounds** (VOCs). Over 500 VOCs have been identified that can be produced by molds, many of which have been determined to be hazardous to human health. These materials are small molecules that evaporate readily at room temperature, which is why they are called *volatile*. Examples of VOCs generated by molds under certain conditions that are known to be hazardous include acetone, benzene, hexane, and methylene chloride. It is the VOCs that may be responsible for the musty odor characteristic of mold.

The irritations caused by molds are generally minor. A typical symptom is minor pain in the irritated area. The area may be red and swollen, and it may feel warmer to the touch than surrounding areas.

The most common effects of the irritations attributed to VOCs appear to be

■ skin rashes or dermititis,
■ soreness and inflammation of the eyes and of the respiratory system,
■ coughing,
■ fatigue,
■ nasal congestion, and
■ post-nasal drip.

In more extreme cases, especially when the individual is particularly sensitive to the VOC, the symptoms may include

■ flu-like symptoms such as nausea and vomiting,
■ decreased attention span,
■ forgetfulness,
■ headaches,
■ dizziness, and
■ difficulty in concentrating.

There are several scientists and physicians who believe that mold cannot produce VOCs in sufficient quantity to result in symptoms. Other physicians, however, believe that a heavy infestation of mold can, indeed, produce such health effects, especially in a sensitive individual.

Allergic Reactions Caused by Molds

By far the most prevalent of the health effects caused by molds are allergic reactions. An **allergy** is a reaction to a small amount of material, or allergen, in the environment that can cause an allergic reaction. The allergen can be pollen, mold, or anything foreign to the sensitive individual. Repeated exposure to the allergen often causes more severe reactions, which become worse with each subsequent exposure to the mold as the individual becomes more sensitized to it.

One reason why allergic reactions to molds are so common is that the cell walls of all molds contain large molecules called **glucans**, which are essentially polymers of the sugar glucose, a little like starch or cellulose. Glucans are known to produce allergic-type reactions. Glucans are inflammatory, and they suppress the immune system when inhaled. The presence of glucans in the cell walls of molds is one of the very few common denominators in these organisms, where there is so much variability in nearly everything else.

Allergies are most common in people who have existing sensitivity to molds or to other allergens, such as pollen, and to people with weakened immune systems. As discussed previously, allergies are also common reactions in people who have been hypersensitized because of repeated exposure to mold, like farmers and others who work around moldy materials or who work or live in mold-infested buildings. Mold antigens can cause **hypersensitivity pneumonitis** (inflammation of the lungs), which can develop into chronic lung disease or **sinusitis**, which is an inflammation of the membranes of the nose and the sinus cavity.

Allergic symptoms may be minor in the case of people with limited exposure to mold or those who are relatively insensitive to the organism. Here, the symptoms are usually mild and short-term. The effect may be very much like hay fever, with nasal stuffiness, runny nose, wheezing, a sore throat, coughing, and itchy eyes. In some cases, there may be some flu-like symptoms.

Allergic reactions are not always minor. In people who are sensitized to mold or suffer from respiratory problems, the symptoms can be much more serious. These more serious reactions can appear as asthma, fever, and/or shortness of breath. In individuals who are already asthmatic, their asthma can be exacerbated by exposure to mold if they are sensitive to mold. In addition to respiratory problems, exposure to mold can result in dermatitis (skin rashes).

Infections Caused by Molds

Infections are the third major type of disease caused by molds. This is the only instance in which household molds ever act as parasites. Generally, molds are **saprophytic**, living only on dead or nonliving material. However, under a few rare circumstances, there are a few species that can become **parasites** and actually grow directly on human tissue.

Molds do not usually cause infections. However, certain species of *Aspergillus* can become parasitic under certain conditions. The three species of *Aspergillus* that are most commonly responsible for causing infections are all Group I molds: *Aspergillus fumigatus*, *Aspergillus flavus*, and *Aspergillus niger*.

None of these species is capable of causing an infection in a healthy individual: healthy people are at minimal risk of infection regardless of their level of exposure to the mold. Because such an infection generally develops only in people with certain pre-existing conditions, the molds causing the infections are sometimes referred to as **opportunistic pathogens**: the pre-existing condition gives the mold the opportunity to act as a pathogen, which is a disease-causing agent.

There are three categories of people who are susceptible to *Aspergillus* infections (called **aspergillosis**): those with (1) chronic sinus infections, (2) immune system deficiencies, and (3) obstructive lung disease. Individuals with any of these conditions have decreased resistance and ability to fight off infection and therefore may be susceptible to aspergillosis.

Aspergillosis develops in about 6 percent of asthmatics who are sensitive to this common mold. In people who have already been afflicted with certain types of lung diseases, such as chronic sinus or lung infections or lung cancer, damage has already been created in the lungs, resulting in cavities. *Aspergillus* can grow in these cavities, thriving on the mucus lining the walls of the larger airways in the lungs of these people. Mold growing in the lungs induces inflammatory and allergic changes in the lung, which can lead to fibrosis and loss of lung function.

Individuals with immunosuppressed or immunocompromised systems, particularly those with cancer, AIDS, or leukemia or recipients of an organ transplant, are also subject to aspergillosis because their bodies cannot produce antibodies to destroy or neutralize the mold antigens that have entered their bodies. As a result, mold invades their lungs and begins growing there, usually inducing pneumonia. If the infection spreads to other organs (such as the heart, brain, eyes, nervous system, skin, and kidneys), the condition is referred to as **invasive aspergillosis**. Nearly any organ or system in the body can be affected.

People with **obstructive lung disease**—such as emphysema or chronic bronchitis that causes a narrowing or obstruction of the airways in the lungs—are also susceptible to aspergillosis. Emphysema and chronic bronchitis are generally caused by smoking. Individuals suffering from obstructive lung disease are also predisposed to aspergillosis.

■ Health Effects of "Toxic" Molds

Molds referred to as "toxic" are molds that produce toxic, or poisonous, chemicals under certain conditions. It is not yet known exactly what conditions induce the production of these chemicals, but a number of factors may be involved, such as light, temperature, moisture, and competition (i.e., the presence of other species of mold and/or bacteria). These chemicals are called **mycotoxins** (*myco* means mold, and *toxin* means poison). Hundreds of mycotoxins are known, but there may be many more that have not yet been identified. Mycotoxins may be carried on spores and on airborne fragments of mycelia.

Several different Group I (and even some Group II) molds are capable of producing mycotoxins under certain circumstances—this capability is certainly not limited to *Stachybotrys chartarum*. In particular, some species of *Aspergillus* and *Penicillium* can produce mycotoxins. For example, several species of *Aspergillus* (in Groups I *and* II) can produce over 100 different mycotoxins. Another relatively common mold, *Fusarium*, can also produce mycotoxins under certain conditions.

There is no doubt that a number of different molds are capable of producing mycotoxins, but few reliable scientific studies have been conducted on these diverse chemicals to establish their health effects upon humans. Therefore, the symptoms reported by the media for people presumably victimized by "toxic" mold are based entirely on only one or, at most, a few, cases. These cases are based largely on conjecture and circumstantial evidence. Scientific studies are not available that demonstrate that mycotoxins—and mold—are definitely responsible for these symptoms. However, a number of lawsuits have been won largely because of the anecdotal reports of the adverse health effects described by the plaintiff.

■ *Stachybotrys*

A number of experts, including some in the real estate industry, have stated that the media have used the term *toxic mold* because it sounds much more interesting—and more frightening—than the word *mold*. Yet, the media nearly always refer *exclusively* to **Stachybotrys chartarum** when they mention toxic mold, although this species of mold is not found nearly as often as are the ten common species of household mold discussed in Chapter 1 as Group II molds. Indeed, two different studies indicated that *Stachybotrys chartarum* is present in only about 2 to 5 percent of the homes examined for such mold, so this species is relatively rare, although it has been found in homes in all 50 states. Furthermore, of the 17 species of *Stachybotrys* known, only this one species (*Stachybotrys chartarum*) is known to produce toxic materials. (Compare this to the ten species of *Aspergillus* and the six species of *Penicillium* that are listed as Group I molds.)

However, because *Stachybotrys chartarum* has received so much media attention, due in large part to court cases, real estate licensees should know something about this mold. It is greenish black and wet and slimy to the touch when it's growing. Whereas *Stachybotrys chartarum* is sometimes called the "black mold," there are other species of "black mold" that are not *Stachybotrys* and not known to produce mycotoxins.

Stachybotrys is generally *not* the mold that lives on plastic, vinyl, or ceramic tiles (although it may be found growing on the cellulose-containing building materials behind those tiles). It is not generally the mold on the grout between shower tiles (but it might be present behind that grout). It is not the green mold found growing on bread and other former goodies living in the refrigerator.

Stachybotrys chartarum needs slightly different conditions to grow than do other molds. Although it requires the same type of substrate (i.e., material high in cellulose content, like wood studs) as is needed by the common household molds, the substrate must be saturated with water. According to Dr. Michael Pinto, *Stachybotrys chartarum* requires either standing water or a relative humidity of at least 90 percent for its spores to germinate, compared to the minimum of 60 percent relative humidity required by many other molds. However, once the spores have germinated, even if the standing water evaporates and the relative humidity drops to 70 percent, *Stachybotrys* will continue to grow. (So, just one flooding event could trigger its growth.)

There is another major difference between the growth of *Stachybotrys chartarum* and that of other molds: *Stachybotrys* needs more time to complete its life cycle than do most other molds. The amount of time required for some common household molds and *Stachybotrys* to colonize (i.e., to grow, reproduce, and spread spores) are:

- *Mucor* and *Rhizopus* (the common bread mold) species: 1 to 2 days
- *Aspergillus* and *Penicillium* species: 2 to 3 days
- *Stachybotrys chartarum:* 8 to 12 days

Much of the media hype about mold and *Stachybotrys chartarum* began with a study performed in Cleveland by Dr. Dorr Dearborn with infants from homes in which water damage from flooding had occurred. Data were collected on 45 infants under six months old who had been diagnosed with acute pulmonary hemorrhage (bleeding from the lungs). According to an update of the original study, 16 of the infants died. Most of these babies lived in water-damaged homes, at least some of which were infested with *Stachybotrys chartarum*. The condition of the infants appeared to be greatly exacerbated by cigarette smoke.

This report is considered controversial because it does not meet the requirements of a scientific study, such as using controls. However, although neither the EPA nor the CDC has validated the study and both agencies maintain that *Stachybotrys* is merely *implicated* in the deaths of the infants, the American Academy of Pediatrics has recommended that pediatricians treating infants with pulmonary hemorrhage ask the parents about mold and water damage in the home and suggests that the parents find and eliminate any sources of moisture that may be present (1998).

Neither the EPA nor the CDC currently supports claims of adverse health effects other than allergies and other respiratory problems from molds. Based on a request from the CDC, the Board on Health Promotion and Disease Prevention of the National Institutes of Health conducted a comprehensive review on the relationship between damp or moldy environments and adverse health effects. Their final report was published in 2004. The review board found sufficient evidence of an association between mold indoors and respiratory problems such as asthma symptoms in sensitized individuals, hypersensitivity pneumonitis in susceptible people, and respiratory illness in otherwise healthy children. However, they concluded that evidence that would establish an association of such health issues as the development of asthma, pulmonary hemorrhage in infants, skin problems, and neuropsychiatric symptoms with mold and/or damp indoor environments is inadequate or insufficient. They also concluded that more research is needed in these areas.

■ Mycotoxins

Neither *Stachybotrys chartarum* nor *any* other mold considered "toxic" produces mycotoxins all the time; they produce these chemicals only under certain conditions. According to the Environmental Health and Safety Department of the University of Minnesota, the right combination of conditions for the production of mycotoxins by *Stachybotrys chartarum* includes

- a relative humidity that is greater than 55 percent,
- fluctuations in temperature (often resulting from turning the thermostat down at night and up during the day), and
- competition from other microorganisms (bacteria and/or other mold).

It is possible that the purpose of mycotoxin production is to inhibit the growth of bacteria and/or other molds in the vicinity of *Stachybotrys chartarum*, an ability that probably evolved because of the relatively slow growth rate of this mold compared to that of other molds.

How does one become exposed to mycotoxins? These chemicals are carried on spores and fragments of mycelia, and they are fat soluble. This means that the mycotoxins are readily absorbed by the digestive system, airways, and skin and that an individual can be exposed to the mycotoxins through the mouth, through inhalation, or by touching a surface that contains the chemical. If someone touches this type of mold and it has been producing mycotoxins, those toxic chemicals can be absorbed through the skin.

Accepted Health Effects of Mycotoxin-Producing Molds

What health effects do mycotoxin-producing molds, such as *Stachybotrys char-tarum*, cause? These molds can cause the same types of general health effects as do many of the nontoxic molds: they can cause or exacerbate allergies, asthma, and infections, without going into mycotoxin-producing mode. (For example, a paper published in the *New England Journal of Medicine* concluded that exposure to an allergen from a species of *Alternaria* does, indeed, constitute a risk factor for respiratory arrest in children and young adults with asthma.) These health effects from mold are well accepted, even by the CDC and the EPA.

What health effects have mycotoxins themselves been *known* to cause? Probably the most definitive cases of diseases in humans beings attributed to mycotoxins have been due to the ingestion of moldy foodstuffs. In one large-scale epidemic in Europe during the Middle Ages, a number of people ingested grains, such as rye, that were contaminated with ergot, a mixture of mycotoxic alkaloids produced by the fungus *Claviceps purpura*, a mold that parasitizes plants. These ergot alkaloids are related to such modern-day wonders as codeine, cocaine, caffeine, nicotine, lysergic acid diethylamide (LSD), and strychnine. Symptoms have been known to range from blistering, gangrene (sometimes resulting in loss of limbs), bizarre behavior, hallucinations, convulsions, and dementia. Ergot poisoning has also been implicated in the behavioral changes that led to the Salem witch trials in 1692.

Under certain conditions, several species of *Aspergillus* produce a mycotoxin called aflatoxin B1, which can cause cancer of the liver in people who have ingested con-taminated peanuts or grain.

Animals have also become ill or even died from eating food contaminated with mycotoxins from molds.

Periodically, a food-related disease has occurred in Russia in association with *Fusarium* molds growing on barley, wheat, and millet that have been allowed to over-winter in the fields. The most recent occurrence occured between 1942 and 1947, during World War II. The grain was contaminated with a trichothecene (or "T-2") mycotoxin; ingestion of the T-2-contaminated grain resulted in a mortality rate of 10–60 percent of the local population.

The T-2 mycotoxins, which can be produced by several species of molds, are par-ticularly hazardous. It is possible that some of these mycotoxins have been used in biological warfare, such as in the "yellow rain" attacks in Cambodia, Afghanistan, and Iraq. Direct contact with T-2 can cause severe eye and skin irritations. In larger doses, individuals can be incapacitated and can die within minutes or hours after exposure.

Alleged Health Effects of Mycotoxins and Mycotoxin-Producing Molds

The major area of contention from scientists is usually focused on health effects caused by mycotoxins taken into the body through inhalation. According to Dr. Nathan Yost, the problem is not a lack of belief that some molds can produce chemicals that can make people sick; rather, it is disagreement as to whether enough of those chemicals can enter the body through inhalation of mold spores and mycelial fragments in a moldy building to cause the symptoms and abnormalities alleged by these individuals.

In addition, much of the controversy about health effects that may be caused specifically by mycotoxins has arisen because of the fact that many of the health effects allegedly caused by mycotoxins and reported by the media cannot be substantiated by scientific research. Some of the allegations may be correct, but they have not been proven. Yet, a number of juries have been persuaded to award large sums of money to plaintiffs because of health problems allegedly caused by mold, even without scientific proof.

All these factors increase the difficulty of establishing scientifically sound cause-and-effect relationships between mycotoxins and health in humans. This is especially true since the list of possible health effects, particularly anecdotal reports reported by the media, is so long and diverse. Furthermore, there are no current tests available for testing for mycotoxins in humans or animals. To complicate the issue even more, researchers do not yet have any good analytical tools for measuring mycotoxins, and it is unknown how much of any given mycotoxin is required to induce health effects—no such studies have been performed on humans, for obvious reasons.

So the major area of concern for the EPA and the CDC pertaining to mycotoxins relates to the toxins being taken into the body by inhalation rather than through ingestion. Let's look at some of the lawsuits and their allegations of adverse health effects.

In several lawsuits relating to mold infestations, particularly of *Stachybotrys chartarum*, the health effects described often include:

- Nosebleeds
- Bleeding in the lungs
- Coughing up large chunks of blood

Some people reported other symptoms from various molds, such as:

- Dizziness and loss of equilibrium
- Nausea, vomiting, and diarrhea
- Fatigue and/or a general malaise—just feeling "yucky"
- Damage to internal organs (liver, kidney, blood, lungs)
- Central nervous system damage, including:
  - Short-term memory loss
  - Attention-deficit problems
  - Tremors
- Personality changes (such as irritability or depression)
- Suppression of the immune system
- Cancer

As in the case of other types of molds, however, the effects of toxic molds such as *Stachybotrys chartarum* vary. For example, a home in Albuquerque was infested with *Stachybotrys*, yet none of the family members suffered any ill effects. Possible explanations are:

- The species of *Stachybotrys* was one of the types for which no health hazards have been reported.
- The conditions were not right for mycotoxin production.
- Insufficient mycotoxin was produced to cause health effects.
- The family members were resistant to the effects of the mold.

Again, the problems relate primarily to the lack of scientific studies, particularly controlled experiments, and lack of evidence of the amounts of mycotoxins that are produced by different molds under varying conditions. The situation is complicated, not only by the inherent variability of people and their susceptibility to mold, but also by the great range of chemicals produced by different species of mold and those that are produced under varying circumstances. Until thorough scientific studies are performed to determine the effects of all these variables, it is doubtful whether organizations such as the CDC and the EPA will accept the anecdotal evidence of symptoms that has been provided in lawsuits to date.

■ Recovery from Mold-Induced Illness

Fortunately, some of these reactions to molds appear to be reversible—that is, if you remove the sick person from the mold source, he or she often recovers—the symptoms may disappear totally.

In one case in Albuquerque, a mother told a friend of hers, a real estate agent, that she was finally ready to buy a house—and that she "might need to hurry." She was disgusted with her landlord's refusal to maintain her apartment in good repair—the roof leaked and was never fixed right. Her biggest concern, however, was for her daughter, who had been sick for a year and suffered from asthma. She told her friend that the wallpaper in her daughter's room was beginning to peel, and she thought that mold was behind the wallpaper. Mold *was* found under the wallpaper, just a few feet away from the girl's bed. A doctor had ordered a humidifier for the girl's room, which made the situation worse since it added more moisture to the room.

In less than 30 days, a house had been found for the mother and her daughter. They closed and moved in 60 days. Just four months after moving out of the apartment, the mother reported to her friend that her daughter was healthier than she had been in over a year, with no more signs of asthma. Even the family dog, who had been chronically sick in the apartment, recovered after moving to the home. (The mother never exhibited any health problems at all.)

In another case, a seven-year-old boy was diagnosed with inflammation of his lungs. *Stachybotrys* was found in fluid used to rinse out his lungs and was also found in his water-damaged home. After the boy was removed from his home and the home was cleaned, he recovered completely.

Often people who live in a mold-infested house will feel fine when they go away on vacation. Then they come back home, and the illness begins again. Many of these health effects appear to be reversible if the mold problem is remediated or the people move out early enough. However, if too much damage has been done to the tissues of the body, the infected individual will probably continue to have some health problems but may improve somewhat. Whether or not such damage is reversible in any given individual depends upon the resistance of the person and the type and severity of damage done to that person's body. This is another area in which research is needed.

◼ Possible Change in Direction in Mold-Related Claims and Lawsuits

It is likely that the balance between the "win-loss" column is shifting in mold-related claims and lawsuits. Until just recently, there was no clear distinction between whether the plaintiff alleging health problems from mold would win or whether the defendant (insurance company, real estate broker, landlord, etc.) would win in any one of these cases. In the wake of a report published in 2002, however, it looks as if the balance is changing to favor the defendants in many of these cases. The reason is a position paper, published by the American College of Occupational and Environmental Medicine (ACOEM) in 2002, *Adverse Human Health Effects Associated with Molds in the Indoor Environment*. Although this paper acknowledges an association of mold and mold spores with mold-induced allergies, infections, and irritations, it takes issue as to whether inhaled mycotoxins can be responsible for the myriad of clinical signs that have been attributed to them in the residential or office settings described in most of these claims and lawsuits. According to the ACOEM, "current scientific evidence does not support the proposition that human health has been adversely affected by inhaled mycotoxins in home, school, or office environments" (p. 4). This paper has become a tool used by the defense in litigation. If the health issue is considered to be caused by mycotoxins, the plaintiff's case may be discredited because of it.

For example, Colin and Pamela Fraser moved into a New York City apartment and began to suffer headaches, rashes, fatigue, and respiratory infections, which they attributed to mold. They brought suit against their landlord (they lived in a cooperative). The court refused to allow their medical expert to testify that mold caused their problems because the state trial judge informed them that their allegation was "unsupported by the scientific literature" (i.e., the ACOEM paper).

An extensive review of the literature was commissioned by the CDC and prepared by the Institute of Medicine (IOM) of the National Academy of Sciences. The authors of this book also could not find sufficient evidence to support the claims of "toxic mold syndrome" (i.e., illness alleged to exposure to mycotoxins) in an extensive review of the literature. This book, *Damp Indoor Spaces and Health*, was released in 2004 and is also being used by defendants in mold-related lawsuits. An example is a case (*Kilian v. Equity Residential Trust*) that was brought before the U.S. District Court for Arizona in 2004. In this case, the plaintiff claimed that mold in her apartment caused her to develop a brain injury, a disorder of her immune system, seizures, problems with movement, and neurocognitive problems. The court rejected her medical claim and ruled "that there is insufficient evidence of an association between neuropsychiatric symptoms and the presence of mold." ("Inadequate or insufficient evidence" are the key buzzwords used in this IOM book.)

Eventually, enough research may be conducted to resolve the issue of whether inhaled mycotoxins can cause the problems attributed to them in these court cases, enough to satisfy the CDC, the EPA, the IOM, the ACOEM, and any other organization that may be relevant. Until then, it would be wise for plaintiffs to focus on those health effects that are not being questioned (i.e., infections, allergies, and irritations) although the courts may discredit even these clinical signs, as in the Fraser lawsuit discussed here.

■ Why It's Difficult for Physicians to Diagnose Mold-Induced Illnesses

Adverse health effects caused by molds have been very hard for physicians to diagnose because of the wide range of clinical signs, or symptoms, that can result from exposure to mold and/or mycotoxins. Coupled with the wide range of symptoms is the fact that most physicians have not been aware of the problem—and there are currently no clinical tests that can be done for mold or for mycotoxins other than testing an individual for susceptibility to specific mold allergens. In addition, no *biomarkers* for mold are known. **Biomarkers** are chemicals in the body that indicate whether an individual has been exposed to a particular disease-causing organism or condition. They are used in the diagnosis of many forms of cancer and for asthma and make it possible to determine the progress of disease and/or the effect of treatment on the disease. Therefore, it has been very difficult to prove any correlation between exposure to mold and symptoms.

Now, however, there is a book available that provides guidance for physicians to diagnose potentially mold-related conditions. The book, *Guidance for Clinicians on the Recognition and Management of Health Effects Related to Mold Exposure and Moisture Indoors*, was written by Dr. Eileen Storey et al. and published by the Center for Indoor Environments and Health at the University of Connecticut (UConn) Health Center with a grant from the EPA. The 120-page book was published on September 30, 2004, and can be downloaded for free at *www.oehc.uchc.edu/CIEH.asp*. The document was designed to help physicians identify patients that may have mold- or moisture-related illnesses. It includes a number of case reports and information about mold. It also provides a questionnaire that physicians can have the patient fill out to determine the possibility of mold and/or moisture problems that may lurk in the patient's home or work environment.

A number of physicians are taking a very practical approach. Although they are not contesting the views of either the IOM or the ACOEM, they are recommending that anyone considered to be at risk from mold be removed from any contaminated areas and not be brought back until the cause of moisture has been determined, the moisture eliminated, and the mold cleaned up.

■ Chapter Four Review Questions

1. The effects of mold can include
   a. gradual destruction of PVC tubing.
   b. breakdown of cellulose-containing materials and loss of the structural integrity of the building materials.
   c. breakdown of glucans.
   d. deterioration of copper pipes.

2. Which statement regarding an individual's responses to mold is *FALSE*?
   a. They vary with his or her health.
   b. They vary with the type of mold.
   c. They vary with the conditions to which the mold has been exposed.
   d. They do not vary.

3. The primary factor determining a person's vulnerability to mold usually involves
   a. allergies.
   b. asthma.
   c. any respiratory diseases.
   d. a weakened immune system.

4. A response that would *NOT* typically be attributed to common household molds is
   a. coughing up blood.
   b. allergies.
   c. irritations.
   d. flu-like symptoms.

5. Many volatile organic compounds (VOCs) are produced by molds and may be responsible for the onset of infections.
   a. True
   b. False

6. The *MOST* common single health effect caused by mold is
   a. infection.
   b. irritation.
   c. allergy.
   d. asthma.

7. Skin rashes are typical symptoms caused by
   a. mycotoxins.
   b. VOCs.
   c. glucans.
   d. aspergillosis.

8. An infection from mold could develop in vulnerable individuals who have inhaled spores of
   a. *Stachybotrys.*
   b. *Aspergillus.*
   c. *Penicillium.*
   d. *Alternaria.*

9. Mycotoxins
   a. are produced all the time by mycotoxin-producing molds.
   b. are produced only by *Stachybotrys.*
   c. have been proven to cause very serious diseases.
   d. may be produced by some molds in response to the presence of other molds or bacteria.

10. *Stachybotrys*
    a. germinates more rapidly than most other household molds.
    b. requires more time to complete a life cycle than most other household molds.
    c. produces mycotoxins as soon as it germinates.
    d. is appropriately called "black mold" or "the toxic mold."

Inspection and Remediation

learning objectives

After completing this chapter, you will be able to

- describe the possible "mold scenarios" that may occur in a home;

- identify when testing and/or sampling may be necessary;

- explain when you can clean up a mold problem yourself and when the situation calls for professional assistance; and

- summarize how a mold problem that has already been cleaned up may return.

■ Key Terms

AHHS	false positives	QPCR
DOHMH	HVAC systems	remediation
ERMI	MSQPCR	test kits
false negatives	PCR	

In the best of all possible worlds, buildings do not have visible mold, your buyer will not discover mold in his or her newly purchased home, and your own home will be relatively mold-free. However, this is not always the way it works.

■ Yes, There Is Mold in Your Home

Between May 2005 and March 2006, the EPA and HUD conducted a national survey of housing-related hazards—the American Healthy Homes Survey (**AHHS**). As part of this survey, they tested mold levels in 1,100 residences across the United States. (Because mold is a natural part of our outdoor environment, it is natural to find it present in equal amounts indoors, as well.) It should come as no surprise, therefore, that the AHHS revealed the presence of mold in 100 percent of the homes surveyed. It is safe to assume, then, that there is also mold in the home of your seller and in the home that your buyer wants to purchase.

Several different mold scenarios can be going on in a house at any given time. A few of the more common scenarios follow:

■ A home may have levels of mold spores that are similar to outdoor levels. Mold is not visible and enters and exits the home through open doors and windows, which presents no problem as long as humidity levels are not too high.

■ Small quantities of a mold-like substance are visible. This is not a problem if it is taken care of promptly. For example, small patches of mold or a mold-like substance on bathroom tiles can be washed away with soap and water. Moisture levels can easily build up in bathrooms, which is why it is important to run the exhaust fan when showering or bathing.

■ The home may have hidden mold. This is a problem that can easily get out of hand. Many times, the mold is hidden behind a wall and is due to a leak or some other hidden event.

■ A mold-like substance is visible, easy to detect, and may be an obvious problem if the substance is indeed mold.

If a mold-like substance is discovered in a home, there is no cause for panic. A bit of calm investigation may reveal that the material is not mold at all, but something else entirely—such as candle soot, dirt, or a stain. Even if the material does turn out to be mold, most people are not overly sensitive to it at low levels. The key to preventing minor mold issues from becoming major problems is education. Teaching people to monitor and correct any moisture issues as soon as they are detected is the best weapon against mold development because, without moisture, there can be no mold growth.

■ Sampling and Testing

How do you know if you need to have a home tested or sampled for mold? If you see something that you suspect is mold, there is generally no reason to test it. Simply clean it up if it is in a small area and make sure there is no longer a source of moisture.

Taking air or surface samples and sending them to a laboratory for mold tests should only be considered

■ when a person living in a home or a member of the buyer's family is particularly susceptible to mold because of respiratory problems or previous exposure to it;

■ when there is a historic record (such as a CLUE report) of a moisture or a mold problem in a home (see Chapter 7 for a discussion of CLUE reports);

■ when it's necessary to ensure that a house being listed is clean after remediation of a mold infestation; and

■ when the buyer has requested mold sampling and testing.

Test Kits

Test kits, generally available at hardware stores or online for under $10, usually consist of a nutrient medium that is attached to some kind of a stick or paddle. The user places it in such a way that the medium comes into contact with the suspect area. The user then places the sample in a closed container and ships it off to a lab.

These kits are subject to various control problems when used by inexperienced persons. Test kits can give **false positives**, which means that they "detect" mold that may not really be a problem because it may be at about the same level as the amount of mold outdoors—or even lower. Samples should be taken indoors and outdoors so that an accurate comparison can be made. If the level indoors is less than or approximately the same as the level outdoors, the test results would suggest that there is no current mold problem.

A further problem with many test kits is the risk of a **false negative**—the failure to detect mold that *is* present in the area. For example, a home could have a heavy infestation of *Stachybotrys* on a windowsill or in other key locations throughout the residence. However, if the mold is still wet and slimy, it will not yet be capable of releasing spores, so any testing done *of the air* will give low readings. Mold on the windowsill can, of course, be easily sampled—but what if the mold is hidden? In this case, you would get a false negative reading when, in fact, your home is about to become a hotbed of mold activity as soon as the mold mass dries out sufficiently to release its spores.

A number of test kits rely on collecting samples from a Petri dish (a flat, round dish) containing some kind of medium. These are ineffective because they depend on spores floating around in the air to land on the medium. Because the spores are so light, they may not land, at least not in the Petri dish.

Standard Methods of Sampling and Testing

If sampling and testing are deemed necessary, have the work done by a professional who has experience in developing and carrying out sampling protocols and who can interpret the results obtained. (See Chapter 7 for suggestions on how to find a professional to do the sampling and testing in accordance with the Indoor Environmental Standards Organization, or IESO.)

Currently, a large percentage of all mold samples is collected from the air. Trained inspectors use a calibrated pump to collect a metered amount of air through a spore trap; they then send the spore trap to an accredited microbiology laboratory for analysis.

According to Thad Godish, professor of Natural Resources and Environmental Management at Ball State University, the only reasonably reliable methods of determining concentrations of mold in air in residences and other buildings are those using "dynamic sampling methods, that is, techniques that use samplers with air pumps and an appropriate collection medium" used by professionals.

Hiring a professional to sample for mold and send the samples to a reputable laboratory for testing is usually considered the best option if testing is necessary. The professional is familiar with the appropriate sampling protocols and equipment. However even a professional may not be able to find anything at the time of sampling, though he or she will know where to look and what to look for. It is important to remember that mold is sometimes hidden. As a result, even mold testing by the best and most experienced professionals may fail to detect evidence of mold or spores, and there may be no evidence of water damage.

ERMI and the Polymerase Chain Reaction

As of November 2007, a new technology was made available to environmental professionals who conduct testing to determine if a home has a high probability of mold growth. The Environmental Relative Moldiness Index (**ERMI**) is a combination of EPA research, a new method of screening homes for mold, and a powerful new analytical method based on DNA analysis.

The EPA developed a method of analysis using the best technology available to identify mold accurately. That method is called the mold-specific quantitative polymerase chain reaction (**MSQPCR**) test, a highly specific DNA-based method for quantifying mold species. Quantitative **PCR (QPCR)** is now used in many fields of science, such as genetics and cancer research. The technology directly probes the DNA of mold with 99 percent accuracy to detect whether the target species of mold are present and how many spores of each species are contaminating the indoor environment.

The EPA found that every indoor environment harbors a stable mold reservoir—dust. All buildings contain some level of dust. By analyzing the DNA in that dust for mold, the historical record is reflected in the ERMI. The ERMI is simply a score based on the amounts of Group I (water intrusion) versus Group II molds (common) that were discussed in Chapter 1.

Data from this collected dust narrowed down the total number of approximately 100 mold species found to 36 indicator molds that seem to grow indoors. As discussed in Chapter 1, the 36 species were subdivided into two very different groups of mold: Group I and Group II molds. Group II molds are the 10 species of mold found to be common in most homes and in low concentrations. Occupants living and working in indoor environments that contained predominantly Group II molds were healthy and suffered few respiratory illnesses, and the homes showed no evidence of leaks or water intrusion. The Group I molds (26 species) were found in homes with visible mold growth and a history of water damage or water intrusion due to lack of maintenance, poor construction, or leaking pipes. Occupants of these homes and environments typically suffered respiratory and asthma-related illnesses.

> Regardless of whether sampling and testing is performed, the source of any leak that has led to mold growth should be found and fixed before remediating (cleaning up) the mold. Otherwise, the mold will come back.

The ERMI score from the DNA analysis of dust lets a building owner or homeowner know whether his or her home or building contains Group II molds, like the rest of the healthy homes identified in the EPA study, or if it is contaminated by Group I mold species, where water intrusion and respiratory problems are common. An additional benefit to using the ERMI sampling protocol is the fact that only one sample is collected per structure, and no baseline sample from outdoors is needed. This is particularly beneficial during periods of poor outdoor weather conditions. One detriment in using the ERMI sampling protocol is the high cost of laboratory analysis and the fact that the thousands of mold species beyond the 36 target species are ignored in the analysis. Overall, however, the ERMI is a very effective screen that is easy to use. It gives a general historic record of the "moldiness" of a home, whereas traditional air sampling merely gives a current record of airborne mold.

The disadvantages and benefits of each method could fill pages of text. The bottom line is that professional mold inspections and other indoor environmental quality investigations require ongoing study. Just make sure that the inspector you choose to help your clients is trained and certified in the current methods.

■ General Mold Cleanup Procedures

Cleanup in Small Areas

The EPA defines a "small area" of mold as about 10 square feet, or an area that is about 3' × 3'. The New York City Department of Health and Mental Hygiene (**DOHMH**), which has developed an excellent and widely used set of procedures for cleaning up mold infestations of varying sizes, uses this same definition. If the mold is limited to a relatively small area, you can probably clean it up easily if you are not sensitive to the mold, if you act before the mold can infest a greater area, and if you use the following suggestions provided by the EPA in their brochure *A Brief Guide to Mold, Moisture, and Your Home* (EPA 402-K-02-003).

To avoid breathing in mold or mold spores, the EPA recommends that you wear an N-95 respirator. Such a respirator can be purchased for about $12 to $25 online or at some hardware stores. Some of these N-95 respirators look like paper dust masks, and some have a nozzle on the front. Others are made mostly of plastic or rubber and have removable cartridges that trap most of the mold spores. Note that these respirators must fit the individual's face properly and have no air leaks in order to be effective. If a fitness test of this respirator is not performed, improper use of the mask can lead to serious health risks. Some environmental companies and some clinics perform these tests, as do some of the stores in which the respirators are sold.

Wear goggles, preferably ones without ventilation holes, so that you do not get mold or mold spores in your eyes.

> Whatever you use, **NEVER mix bleach and any household product containing ammonia!** Ammonia and bleach will react to form chlorine gas, which is far more deadly than mold!

There is some controversy in the literature as to the best solution to use to clean up mold. Although the Centers for Disease Control (CDC) suggests using bleach and water, the EPA recommends use of a mild detergent and water instead, in part because of the hazardous nature of bleach and its fumes. In fact, on page 15 of its brochure about mold, the EPA states "The use of a chemical or biocide that kills organisms such as mold (chlorine bleach, for example) is not recommended as a routine practice during mold cleanup." Bleach is effective as a disinfectant, but it is often overused and therefore may create additional air quality issues.

Avoid touching the mold or any mold-contaminated items with your bare hands. Wear rubber gloves, preferably long ones that extend to the middle of your forearms. If using a mild detergent, as recommended by the EPA, ordinary rubber gloves will suffice. However, if you are using a disinfectant, chlorine bleach, or a strong cleaning solution, use gloves made of natural rubber, nitrile, neoprene, polyurethane, or PVC.

Hard, nonporous surfaces (such as bathroom tile) with a growth of mold can often be wiped clean. Scrub mold off these surfaces with your cleaning agent (such as detergent and water) and dry the surfaces completely. Cleaning often works on nonporous material unless mold is also harbored in porous materials behind it. If the mold is localized to a relatively small patch living on porous material, it may be sufficient to clean it; if it comes back, however, or if it is extensive, it is preferable to remove and replace the affected materials. Simply killing the mold will not necessarily eliminate all risks since even fragments of mold or dead spores can still trigger immunoresponses in individuals.

If the contaminated surfaces are absorbent or porous, such as ceiling tile, wallboard (or sheetrock), or carpet, those materials should be thrown away and replaced. Because of the porosity of these materials, mold can grow in the spaces, or pores, so it may be impossible to remove it completely. Cleaning and repainting such materials as mold-infested wallboard or ceiling tile is usually not enough because the mold has eaten into the cellulose material of the food source, and dormant spores undoubtedly remain. Check what is on the other side of the wall to make sure there is no massive infestation that has been hidden.

Don't try to take shortcuts—never paint or caulk moldy surfaces. Replace porous materials or clean up nonporous building materials and let them dry before painting them. If you paint moldy surfaces, the paint will probably peel, and the mold is very likely to come back.

Cleanup in Larger Areas

If the water damage is extensive and/or if the mold infestation is greater than 10 square feet, you should refer to the EPA's guide *Mold Remediation in Schools and Commercial Buildings*. You can get a free copy by calling the EPA Indoor Air Quality Information Clearinghouse at 800-438-4318, or you can download it at *www.epa.gov/iaq/molds/publications.html*.

The procedures developed by the DOHMH of New York City (which can be found at their Web site, *www.nyc.gov/html/doh/html/epi/moldrpt1.shtml*) provide recommendations for cleaning up five different levels of mold infestations based on the size of the infestation. These are some of the most definitive procedures available for mold **remediation** (cleanup). Level I was covered in the previous section under *Clean-up in Small Areas* (10 square feet or less).

According to the DOHMH, Level II consists of midsized isolated areas, each of which would range from 10 to 30 square feet. In addition to the protective equipment recommended by the EPA in their brochure (respiratory protection, goggles, and gloves), the work area should be covered with a plastic sheet and sealed with tape before cleanup activities begin in order to contain dust and debris. Dust suppression methods, such as misting (*not* soaking) surfaces prior to remediation are also recommended. Contaminated materials that cannot be cleaned should be removed from the building in sealed plastic bags, which can then be disposed of in the trash. The work area and any areas used to exit the work area should be vacuumed with a machine equipped with a high-efficiency particulate air (HEPA) filter and cleaned with a damp cloth or mop and a detergent solution. When the work is finished, the area should be left dry and visibly free of contamination and debris.

Any infested area larger than 30 square feet should be cleaned by professionals using protocols developed for the specific project and with more extensive personal protective equipment. For Levels III through V, a health and safety professional with appropriate experience should be consulted to provide project oversight. Level III covers large isolated areas (30 to 100 square feet), such as several wallboard panels. Level IV procedures are for extensive contamination (greater than 100 contiguous square feet in an area), and Level V pertains to remediation of heating, ventilation, and air-conditioning (**HVAC**) **systems**.

Obtaining Professional Assistance

If the mold covers an area larger than 10 square feet or you are sensitive to mold, you would be well advised to bring in professional assistance to clean it. Be sure the person or company who is conducting the remediation work is a professional with experience in mold, and ask for (and verify) references. Observe the following precautions.

- Acquire more than one bid—remediation and repair of your home can cost thousands of dollars. Bids should be in writing and should describe all the work that will be done.
- Ask to see their operating procedures that specifically address mold remediation.
- Do not choose a company that will not guarantee their work, and get the warranty in writing before the contract is signed.
- Make sure they are bonded.
- Ask to see proof of insurance.
- If you have testing done, hire a different company to do the remediation.
- Review the bids with your insurer to determine which costs will be covered by your policy and which ones you will have to pay for.

Post-Remediation: Will the Mold Return?

What happens *after* you have cleaned up a mold infestation? Can the mold come back? It might. Cleaning *will* kill the mycelia. Any spores that have been activated by moisture and have begun to germinate will probably also be destroyed. What will remain, however, are dormant spores. In fact, if care has not been taken to isolate the mold during remediation activities, the dormant spores may have been spread around, increasing the concentration of mold spores in previously "clean" areas; another episode of flooding or leaking water could cause another infestation. In addition, if mold has penetrated into porous structural materials, its presence can serve as a nucleus for a new infestation if those structural materials get wet again. Many times, a homeowner believes that a mold infestation has been cleaned by the homeowner or by a professional, only to have a new infestation crop up later because the structural materials still harbored dormant spores that were activated as soon as they were exposed to a new (or continuing) source of moisture.

> If the mold has penetrated the building materials, those materials should be replaced during the remediation process. Most building materials are porous, and it is virtually impossible to remove all the mold from them.

Therefore, any structural materials that have been damaged or discolored in a mold infestation should be replaced, especially if they are porous (e.g., wood, carpet, padding, cloth, and wallboard). If they are nonporous, such as ceramic tile, cleaning the mold is usually sufficient if adjacent porous materials have not been contaminated as well. At any rate, the food source remains, and many mold spores will still be present in porous materials that have been only superficially cleaned rather than replaced. Any new source of water can initiate a new mold infestation.

How can you tell when the remediation is finished? According to the EPA's brochure, all visible molds should have been removed, and no musty odors should remain. If a follow-up visit to the mold site shortly after the completion of cleanup reveals no further signs of water damage or mold growth and people reoccupying the building have no mold-related health complaints or physical symptoms, it can be assumed that the remediation has been effective. A wise precaution is to have the cleaned area tested by taking samples and sending them to an independent accredited laboratory for analysis.

■ Chapter Five Review Questions

1. With respect to mold, the *MOST* desirable condition in a home is that
   a. no mold is present.
   b. indoor levels are similar to outdoor levels, and there is no moisture problem.
   c. mold and moisture problems are hidden.
   d. mold is visible and easy to detect.

2. If you discover a small area of mold in your home, you should
   a. buy a test kit and figure out what kind of mold it is.
   b. hire a professional to clean it up.
   c. leave it alone—it will go away by itself.
   d. consider cleaning it up yourself, following EPA guidelines.

3. At present, the *BEST* method for sampling and testing for mold is to
   a. use a test kit with a stick or a paddle.
   b. use a test kit with Petri dishes.
   c. have a professional collect dust samples and submit them to a lab for a PCR analysis.
   d. have a professional collect air and surface samples indoors, followed by lab testing.

4. If you detect a mold problem, the first thing that you should do is
   a. clean up the mold.
   b. find and stop the leak.
   c. call in a mold expert.
   d. replace all damaged structural materials.

5. According to the EPA, you should seek professional help for a mold cleanup if the damaged area is greater than 5 square feet.
   a. True
   b. False

6. You may consider a mold infestation safely cleaned up if you
   a. have painted over all contaminated porous materials.
   b. have fixed the source of the moisture problem, cleaned the mold from nonporous surfaces, and replaced nonporous contaminated materials.
   c. have cleaned off porous materials with detergent.
   d. cannot detect any visible mold or musty mold-related odors immediately after the remediation has been completed.

7. According to the EPA, the *BEST* cleaner for mold is
   a. bleach.
   b. detergent.
   c. acid.
   d. a strong biocide.

8. The test kits for mold that are available in hardware stores or online for under $10 are generally unreliable and have given too many false positives and false negatives to be trusted.
   a. True
   b. False

9. If the mold-infested area is at least 30 square feet, you should
   a. clean it the same way that you would clean a ten-square foot area.
   b. move out of the property.
   c. call a professional to do the remediation or to advise on the best way for you to clean up the mold yourself.
   d. seal off all doors and windows and sanitize the entire affected surface with a 100 percent solution of bleach.

10. The Environmental Relative Moldiness Index is a combination of EPA research, powerful PCR technology, and a new method for screening homes for mold.
    a. True
    b. False

Policies, Standards, and Legislation

learning objectives

After completing this chapter, you will be able to

- describe the information available about mold on federal Web sites (i.e., the Centers for Disease Control and the Environmental Protection Agency);

- identify the National Association of REALTORS®' recommendations and policies regarding mold infestation;

- describe NAR's concerns and recommendations about mold;

- explain why there are currently no health standards for mold; and

- summarize the key issues considered in the Melina Bill, the legislation proposed in the House of Representatives in 2003.

■ Key Terms

American Conference of Governmental Industrial Hygienists (ACGIH)	health standards Melina Bill	safety standards threshold limit values (TLVs)

■ Federal Organizations

The Centers for Disease Control (CDC) in Atlanta, Georgia, recognizes the public's concern with mold but has not accepted some of the more serious health effects attributed to mold (particularly to mycotoxins) in a number of the lawsuits filed because of the lack of scientific evidence supporting these claims. However, they acknowledge mold's possible contribution to respiratory problems, such as allergies and asthma, irritations, and infections in susceptible individuals.

The CDC's Web site (*www.cdc.gov*) contains a number of articles about mold, including questions and answers about *Stachybotrys chartarum* and other molds, molds in the environment, and asthma.

In July 2002, the Environmental Protection Agency (EPA) published *A Brief Guide to Mold, Moisture, and Your Home* (EPA 402-K-02-003). This brochure provides information for homeowners and renters on mold basics, hidden mold, how to prevent mold growth, and how to clean up minor residential mold problems. The brochure is available online (*www.epa.gov/iaq/molds/moldguide.html*) or can be ordered free of charge from the EPA by calling 800-438-4318. (Ask for the brochure by its number, EPA 402-K-02-003.) Although it is not currently required by law, it is recommended that real estate licensees give a copy of the brochure to their buyers and sellers (see also Chapter 7). The brochure is also available in Spanish.

In addition to the brochure, the EPA's Web site also has a mold resources page that provides considerable information about mold and a document entitled *Mold Remediation in Schools and Commercial Buildings,* which discusses methodology to be used in cleaning up large mold infestations in residences, schools, public buildings, and other commercial facilities. The Web page that pertains to mold is *www.epa.gov/iaq/molds.*

■ The National Association of REALTORS®

Along with the CDC and the EPA, the National Association of REALTORS® (NAR) was one of the first organizations to become concerned about "toxic" mold in homes. NAR has placed a number of articles and reports relating to mold on its Web site. Although some of it is available only to REALTORS®, some excellent background material may be accessed by NAR nonmembers by going to the NAR Web site at *www.realtor.org* and typing in "mold" in the search window.

The NAR Risk Management Committee was so concerned about "toxic" mold that it formed a Mold Working Group in the spring of 2001. The working group consists of 13 members and a committee liaison and was charged with both evaluating the information available on mold and developing recommendations for actions that NAR could take to assist members in dealing with this problem. In the *Report of the Mold Working Group of the Risk Management Committee,* published in April 2002 and available to NAR members online at *www.realtor.org,* the following recommendations were made.

■ Seller disclosures need to be refined to include mold and water intrusion.

■ NAR should encourage state associations to advocate the adoption of laws to provide a defense to claims against real estate brokers and property managers who disclosed any known moisture and mold problems and provided buyers/tenants with appropriate disclosure information regarding mold. Where no such laws have been adopted, NAR should research measures to recommend that real estate professionals use to minimize their liability for mold infestations.

■ NAR should review the availability of errors and omissions (E&O) insurance for real estate professionals for claims based on health effects or property damage associated with mold and should work with the insurance carriers and/or seek legislative relief to avoid any interruption of such insurance.

■ NAR should work with other groups to encourage the development of information pertaining to methods for remediating mold, which may include new construction materials and methods.

■ NAR should conduct educational programs for its members regarding mold and its impact on real estate as soon as possible.

Problems recognized by the NAR Mold Working Group include:

■ Mold is everywhere—and mold problems can grow quickly.

■ Tests may not be accurate.

■ There are no standards defining a "safe" level of mold.

■ Preparing disclosures is difficult because of the lack of a standard specifying a safe level of mold.

■ NAR, through its Risk Management Committee, should continually monitor whether moisture and mold disclosures result in pricing and financial constraints for properties, including lower property values, increased lender requirements for insurance, and affordability of property insurance.

■ NAR should support federal indoor air quality research on mold and its health effects and should disseminate the objective scientific results of the research. NAR should also support efforts to educate homeowners regarding their responsibility to identify and disclose any known environmental hazards, including mold, to agents, brokers, and buyers.

■ NAR should encourage the development of a consumer-oriented informational brochure that accurately portrays the real-estate-related issues raised by mold. (This recommendation has been met in part by the EPA's publication of their brochure, *A Brief Guide to Mold, Moisture, and Your Home*, although real-estate-related issues are not addressed in the brochure.)

■ NAR should investigate current practices and monitor conditions that affect the availability of property insurance, such as mold. NAR should also encourage state associations to find regulatory relief to avoid any interruption in the availability of that insurance because of mold.

■ NAR should facilitate the compilation of research regarding mold, including health effects, determination of "safe" levels of mold, and mold detection and remediation techniques.

■ Why There Are No Health Standards for Mold

Nearly all health and **safety standards** originate in the workplace because of injuries or deaths occurring there and because records are kept on these events. Because mold has never been considered a workplace hazard—there are no known reports of any worker dying because of a mold-related accident—and because there are no existing industrial data on the health effects of mold, no health or safety standards for mold have been set.

Real estate professionals are accustomed to having some type of federal safety standards upon which to base disclosure statements. Unfortunately, there are no health or safety standards for mold as there are for the lead content of lead-based paint or for the amount of radon present in a home.

Health standards are often referred to as **threshold limit values (TLVs)**. TLVs can be used as guidelines for determining the appropriate level of protection needed against a hazardous material. There are several different types of TLVs, but they are beyond the scope of this book because no TLVs have been established for mold.

It is important to remember that mold is a biological organism—which means that the health effects of mold are highly variable: they vary with species, the amount of mold, the conditions to which the mold is exposed, and even the presence or absence of bacteria or other species of molds. When coupled with the variability of human responses to mold, the moving target factor that was discussed earlier is intensified—now, the target is moving randomly, with no pattern whatsoever—and setting standards for mold becomes increasingly difficult. Even Dr. Stephen Redd, chief of Air Pollution and Respiratory Health of the Centers for Disease Control (CDC), speaking at a meeting with a congressional committee in July 2002, acknowledged that setting standards or guidelines for exposure levels of indoor mold may not be practical.

Although there are no TLVs for mold, a type of generic industry standard does exist for "significant" mold levels found by sampling during initial assessments or inspection. A level of ten times more mold in a structure or on a suspect surface when compared to a baseline non-suspect or outdoor sample is considered extraordinary and requires further investigation. This "10-times rule" comes directly from guidance found in the book *Bioaerosols: Assessment and Control*, edited by Janet Macher and published by the **American Conference of Governmental Industrial Hygienists (ACGIH)**. These guidelines are used when interpreting the quantitative characteristics of bioareosol data when no TLVs have been established and constitute only part of a thorough inspection.

Many different climatatic conditions can impact and artificially lower or raise outdoor mold levels, such as snow cover, rain, or even a freshly mowed lawn. Certified inspectors and investigators are trained to take these factors into account when interpreting laboratory data. The high variability of different weather conditions across the United States is another reason the ERMI method discussed in Chapter 5 holds so much promise.

Qualified inspectors and investigators can provide you and your clients with reports that indicate whether significant or extraordinary mold levels may be present. "Exposure limits" and "health standards" are generally considered to be medical issues. If you believe that you have been exposed to significant levels of mold for a prolonged period and you have health concerns, you should see a doctor.

■ Mold-Related Legislation

State Legislation

Some effort is being made to create standards for mold, which is addressed in California's Toxic Mold Protection Act of 2001, signed into law on October 5, 2001. This law states that standards for permissible mold exposure in indoor environments (and for mold assessments and guidelines for the identification and remediation of mold) will be developed "if feasible." One of the two major constraints on whether or not such limits can and will be set is financial—a team has been assembled to look at the issues, but funding for the team is necessary, and the bill does not provide for it. The second constraint has to do with actually setting threshold limits on exposure. Because of the wide variation of susceptibility to mold among individuals and the other sources of deviations described under the "moving target" section of this book, any consensus on setting an exposure limit may take a long time to develop.

The California legislation also requires

- the development of public education materials and resources, and
- a written disclosure of the presence of mold upon the sale or rental of commercial or residential property if the concentration of mold exceeds permissible standards.

The law does *not* require such disclosure, however, if a mold problem was present and was remediated.

Several other states have also passed legislation pertaining to mold, and more are developing such laws. As of July 2003, 58 separate bills had been proposed or passed in 28 states since 2001. A number of states have followed California's lead in its Toxic Mold Protection Act: Massachusetts, Michigan, New Jersey, New Mexico, and New York have all modeled their mold protection acts after California's law. Requirements for disclosures vary from state to state. Topics covered in these state bills generally include

- requests or resolutions to pursue research to determine health risks, study health effects, and/or develop health standards for mold;
- regulation of mold assessors and remediators;
- procedures for insurers to use in handling water damage claims;
- requirements for certain insurance companies regarding mold coverage;
- preparation of a plan for testing and remediating mold in public schools;
- requirements for studying the presence of mold/fungi in public schools and developing a plan for testing and remediation; and
- provision for reimbursement for remediating mold and other air-quality problems in public schools.

Proposed Federal Legislation: The Melina Bill

Legislation regarding mold has also been proposed at the federal level. Representative John Conyers, Jr., (D-Michigan) introduced a bill into the U.S. House of Representatives on June 27, 2002, due to a case involving the daughter of one of his staff workers who lost 70 percent of her lung capacity because of a mold infestation. This bill is named the U.S. Toxic Mold Safety and Protection Act of 2002 but is often referred to as the **Melina Bill** after the little girl. Congress held its first hearing on mold on July 18, 2002, and several representatives from NAR testified. One object of the hearing was to learn what impact mold has on homeowners, especially the effect of mold upon property values. Representative Conyers reintroduced the bill as H.R. 1268 on March 13, 2003. This bill is scheduled to be reintroduced in 2008.

If the bill is enacted as written, the following requirements would have to be met:

- The Centers for Disease Control (CDC), the Environmental Protection Agency (EPA), and the National Institutes of Health (NIH) will undertake a comprehensive study of the health effects of indoor mold growth and toxic mold.
- The Department of Housing and Urban Development (HUD) will study and report on the impact of construction standards on indoor mold growth.
- A standards development organization will develop standards for building products designed to retard the development of mold.
- The EPA will be required to promulgate national standards for mold inspection, remediation, toxicity testing, and certification of people involved with testing, remediation, and inspection for mold.
- HUD will be required to promulgate guidelines that identify conditions favoring the growth of mold indoors and recommending appropriate means of eliminating those conditions.
- The EPA, CDC, NIH, and HUD will be responsible for sponsoring programs to educate the public about mold.
- Annual inspections of rental properties will be required.
- Prior to the sale or lease of real property, an inspection for mold will have to be conducted by a state-certified mold inspector.
- HUD will be required to promulgate regulations for disclosure of mold hazards in HUD housing that is offered for sale or lease. In addition, HUD must establish procedures to minimize the hazards of indoor mold, including providing mold hazard information pamphlets, periodic risk assessments, mold inspections, testing, and abatement.

- Grants will be made available for the remediation of toxic mold growth in public buildings.
- An insurance program will be established that would enable people to purchase insurance against losses resulting from toxic mold hazards in real property.

■ Chapter Six Review Questions

1. The CDC and the EPA have considerable information about mold available on their Web sites.

   a. True
   b. False

2. Which of the following is *NOT* a recommendation of the NAR's working group on mold?

   a. Seller disclosures should be refined.
   b. Laws are needed to help lessen REALTOR® liability.
   c. Licensees must help buyers decide whether or not they want to buy a home with a mold problem.
   d. Agents should look for water damage in a home.

3. There are currently no health standards for mold (as there are for lead and radon) because

   a. mold has not been an issue and nobody has cared about it until recently.
   b. there is no need for such standards.
   c. extensive data for the effects of mold upon humans are not available.
   d. mold is not really a health issue.

4. To date, the closest anyone has come to setting safety/health standards for mold is the "10-Times Rule," which suggests that a level of ten times more mold in a structure or on a surface compared to an outdoor sample requires further investigation.

   a. True
   b. False

5. The fact that molds are diverse biological organisms is one of the reasons why it is so difficult to set standards.

   a. True
   b. False

6. The Toxic Mold Protection Act passed in California in 2001 requires the development of standards for permissible mold exposure under any circumstances.

   a. True
   b. False

7. The Toxic Mold Protection Act of 2001 requires disclosure of mold upon the sale or rental of residential or commercial property, even if the mold problem was remediated.

   a. True
   b. False

8. The need for disclosure about mold is *NOT* a primary concern

   a. in the California act.
   b. in the Melina Bill.
   c. to the National Association of REALTORS® (NAR).
   d. to the EPA.

9. If the Melina Bill goes through as written, which of the following organizations will *NOT* have responsibilities to fulfill to address the problem of mold?

   a. The National Association of REALTORS® (NAR)
   b. The Environmental Protection Agency (EPA)
   c. The Department of Housing and Urban Development (HUD)
   d. The National Institutes of Health (NIH)

10. The Melina Bill was named for the wife of U.S. Representative John Conyers, Jr. (D-Michigan), who introduced the bill to Congress in 2002.

    a. True
    b. False

Reducing Liability

After completing this chapter, you will be able to

■ describe what to look for in a walk-through inspection, whether you're listing the home or working for a buyer;

■ summarize the information you should give your seller and your buyer about mold;

■ understand what to do and to ask if the seller has had water infiltration (penetration) or mold problems;

■ describe how to find qualified people in the event that you need a mold inspection and/or a mold remediator; and

■ identify the most important steps to take to protect youself and your client from legal liability in case you are involved in a real estate transaction involving water damage and/or mold.

■ Key Terms

American Board of Industrial Hygiene (ABIH)	Certified Industrial Hygienist (CIH)	Council of Engineering and Scientific Specialty Board (CESB)
American Indoor Air Quality Council (AmIAQC)	Comprehensive Loss Underwriting Exchange (CLUE)	Indoor Environmental Standards Organization (IESO)
American National Standards Institute (ANSI)	Council-certified Residential Mold Inspector (CRMI)	

■ How Mold Differs from Other Environmental Red Flags

Unlike lead in paint, the potential for mold infestations is not limited to the age of a home. Mold is everywhere, and it can become a problem anywhere water is allowed to accumulate indoors in areas where it doesn't belong. Also, unlike other environmental hazards, mold does not have a defined safe level because no health standards exist and because there is so much difference in how different people react to mold.

A buyer's or a seller's agent for a home that may have a mold problem should follow the same strategy used for a home that may contain lead paint: ask specific questions of the seller; make sure that the potential buyer receives any pertinent EPA material and other relevant information; and disclose, disclose, disclose.

■ Listing a Home

In an initial walk-through for a home listing, watch for certain signs of water damage and/or mold such as:

- mold and/or water infiltration (referred to as *water penetration* or *water intrusion* in some states) on ceilings, walls, floors, and carpets;
- evidence of leaking pipes, which may be hidden behind bathroom and kitchen walls;
- blistering paint and wallpaper or tiles pulling away from the walls;
- odors—a musty smell signaling the presence of mold that may or not be visible; and
- visible mold, especially in bathrooms.

Even if no mold problems are evident, be sure to discuss mold with your seller and give him or her information such as the EPA brochure and/or any fact sheets issued by your state. At the same time, make sure your seller understands that you are not to be considered an expert on mold.

A relatively small patch of mold (10 square feet or less) can be cleaned with detergent (or bleach) and water, as discussed in Chapter 5 on remediation. There should be a functional exhaust fan or windows that can be used after moisture has accumulated in the room. If mold reappears after cleaning, it may mean that the building materials behind the moldy area have been impregnated with mold and should be replaced. (The most reliable way to ensure that a mold infestation has not returned after it has been cleaned up is by testing.)

If the mold covers a large area (greater than 10 square feet) or if the seller suffers from asthma or other respiratory illnesses, he or she should probably have a professional come in and clean up the mold. (See Chapter 5 on remediation.)

Disclosure Statements

The importance of the accuracy and completeness of the seller's disclosure statement cannot be stressed too much. A seller's complete and accurate disclosure is the agent's and the seller's best protection against liability issues. Questions to ask the seller should include:

- Have you had any water leaks or water damage in your home from flooding, breaking pipes, damaged ice-maker lines, etc.?
- Are you aware of any roof leaks?
- Have you had any leaking pipes?
- Have you had flooding from any of your water-using appliances, such as your dishwasher, washing machine, water heater, or your refrigerator's ice maker?

- Have you had problems with toilet/tub overflows? (Usually, one or two overflows do not present a problem if they were cleaned and dried up right away.)

It may also be a good idea to ask questions like:

- Do you know of any mold in your home?
- Have you tested for mold?

Asking questions is important because the seller may have already forgotten a leak from a washing machine or some other appliance. Even leaks that have been cleaned up may instigate a mold problem under the floor or within the walls.

If the seller has had toilet or tub overflows, check to make sure how quickly they were cleaned up and dried out. If they were not dried out immediately (e.g., within 24 hours), there could be a mold problem. Also, if overflows of this nature are common, the seller might have a plumbing problem, which could result in a mold problem.

If there have been water leakage or water intrusion/penetration problems, they need to be checked out. How quickly were the problems resolved and have they been recurring? If there were only a few such problems and the wet areas were dried out within 24 hours, there should not be a mold problem. Incidents with water damage and/or mold should be handled like a disclosure about termites or lead-based paint. The agent should be aware that

- the problem may have already been solved and there is no issue, or
- the buyer may not care, just as some buyers are not concerned about radon or lead-based paint.

However, the client needs to take care of the water leak or water penetration problem before any mold problem is addressed—mold cannot grow and thrive without a steady source of moisture. Even localized moisture occurring on a regular basis, such as condensation from cool air hitting a warm surface or high humidity from a shower, can result in sufficient moisture to initiate germination of spores and colonization of mold.

Conversations with the seller should be documented for later verification of the completeness and consistency of the disclosure statement against what has been discussed, as well as to provide a record of the conversation should the seller forget any of the points that were discussed.

The seller's agent should read the disclosure statement carefully and have it updated if necessary. Any problems that were discussed should be referenced. The agent should probe to determine if there has been some water penetration event in the past that the seller has forgotten, such as a leaking dishwasher or other appliance. If the seller adds something new, especially something about water leaks, water damage, or mold, the agent should request clarification. Good questions to ask are:

- What was the extent of the water penetration?
- How quickly was it cleaned up?
- Was an insurance claim filed?
- Was any mold detected?
- Was any testing done?

If necessary after clarification, the seller should revise the disclosure statement accordingly.

Many different types of commercial disclosure documents are available, covering everything from mold to radon. Although many of the more reputable environmental disclosure firms, such as Environmental Data Resources Inc., do not specifically disclose the absence or presence of mold, their reports do come with a $20 million dollar insurance policy that protects the agent, broker, seller, and buyer in case a disclosed item on their report is missed. These reports are typically available from the home inspector or environmental consultant at a nominal fee (less than $100). Commercial disclosure statements may cause your sellers to rethink and disclose a minor mold issue they may have elected to "forget." Informed sellers understand that most mold issues are minor and are typically corrected easily when compared to some of the more extreme disclosure items found on an environmental disclosure report.

Comprehensive Loss Underwriting Exchange (CLUE) Program

Many insurance companies now use a data-sharing service known as the **Comprehensive Loss Underwriting Exchange (CLUE)** Program. This data-sharing service is similar to the credit-report services used by lenders to determine the creditworthiness of a potential consumer. With homeowner policies becoming riskier, the CLUE report provides insurance companies with information about homes so that an insurance company can determine its level of risk in insuring a home.

The CLUE database contains approximately 90 percent of the claims filed within the past five years. Homeowners' insurance companies are relying more and more on the information in this database to determine whether they will approve or reject a request for insurance from a buyer.

If any insurance claims were filed for any cause, it may be difficult for the potential buyer to get a homeowners' insurance policy on the home, especially if the claims were for mold or water damage. Ask the seller to provide you immediately with a CLUE report on the home you are listing. The CLUE report will show if, within the last five years, there have been any moisture or mold claims made on the structure or any claims that might be deemed "excessive" by the insurance company. It is better to address this issue up front instead of waiting until escrow.

It is critical that the seller order this report as early as possible. If any claims filed on the home within the last three to five years show up on the CLUE report, it may be difficult or extremely expensive for a potential buyer to obtain the necessary homeowners' insurance, even if the *buyer* has a perfect record. Because homeowners' insurance is required for most home sales, this may kill the sale—sometimes at closing or even afterwards, as insurance companies can deny or even cancel policies up to 60 days after closing. Sometimes insurance can be obtained but is so expensive that the buyer may not be able to afford the additional cost. This, too, may kill the sale.

Only the owner of a home or a participating insurance company can obtain the CLUE report. It can be ordered online for less than $20 from ChoicePoint at *www. choicetrust.com* or by calling 800-456-6004. The biggest advantage of ordering the report online is that you'll receive the report right away; if it is ordered by phone, it may take several weeks.

A potential buyer may ask for the CLUE report or may even make the contract contingent upon receiving it from the seller because this report, which provides information about any claims filed for the property within the last five years, has a strong bearing on the availability of homeowners' insurance.

■ Working with a Buyer

CLUE Report

Buyers should request a copy of the seller's CLUE report early in the transaction. Although the buyer cannot personally order a CLUE report on the seller's home, he or she has the right to examine the report (which can be obtained *only* by the owner of the home) before he or she agrees to buy the home. In fact, the buyer may make the contract contingent upon the receipt of a satisfactory CLUE report on the property. If this isn't done, there could be a nasty surprise at closing if the buyer suddenly discovers that homeowners' insurance is not available (or is too expensive) for that home because of the insurance claims filed on the home or by the seller within the past three to five years. (Most homeowners' insurance companies are now checking the CLUE reports routinely as part of their underwriting process.)

It is also a good idea for the buyer to request a CLUE report on his or her own property, as well. If too many claims have been submitted for the buyer's present home, insurance on another home may also be denied or be very expensive.

Homeowners' Insurance

It has become imperative that buyers begin looking at homeowners' insurance early in the transaction, preferably when they are searching for financing, but sometimes even before they have found a suitable home. The luxury of waiting to find insurance until a few days before closing no longer exists. In fact, it is suggested that, before buyers write an offer for a house, they should get a range of insurance estimates that are reasonable for the price and location of the homes being considered (usually about $400 to $500 per year for a moderately priced home). When writing the offer, the buyer may insert a clause indicating that the sale is subject to the buyer's ability to get affordable insurance that does not exceed a certain amount (e.g., $600 per year for a home in a moderate price range). This gives the buyer an escape clause in the event that only very costly insurance can be obtained.

It may not be possible to find an insurance company that includes mold remediation in its coverage except as a very expensive rider, but some buyers might be interested in purchasing such a policy. Buyers must tell their insurance professional what they want in homeowners' insurance. High-risk insurance pools are available in most states, so insurance is not usually impossible to find—just expensive. Sometimes, however, no insurance can be purchased for a home with claims, particularly if the claims were for hail, water damage, mold, or even burglary.

Extending the Right to Terminate the Contract

During the walk-through of the home with your buyer, pay particular attention to any evidence of water damage and/or mold. Use your eyes and your nose—any musty odors are a red flag and should be investigated.

Educate the Buyer

Buyers need to be educated about mold, especially if there are signs of mold or water damage. Agents should give their clients any available fact sheets about mold, along with the EPA's brochure on mold, but they should make it clear that they are not experts on the subject. A number of states (e.g., Arizona, California, New Mexico, and New York) have developed fact sheets about mold, which can be given to buyers as well. Buyers may be referred to relevant Web sites, such as the EPA and the Centers for Disease Control (CDC) sites. If the purchase agreement has an objection clause, the buyer may object by the objection deadline.

Inspections

The buyer should be present during any inspections so that the inspector can explain any problems directly to him or her. It is also a good idea these days to ask the inspector to pay particular attention to any signs of water damage. If a termite inspection is done, that inspector should also be asked to watch for signs of water penetration, because these inspectors poke around in places where general inspectors might not go and because mold and termites often favor the same conditions. Many inspectors do not inspect or test for mold but will tell the buyer about any unusual discolorations or growths that the buyer might want to have tested.

Consistent Treatment of Everyone

The agent must remember to treat everyone the same under the Fair Housing Act. Even if the buyer has an obvious problem with asthma, he or she should not be treated any differently from anyone else. If an agent tells everyone about the potential problems with mold in a home that exhibits signs of water damage and/ or mold, he or she will not be violating the law if the asthmatic person understands the possible health problems with the house. That way, the agent will be fulfilling his or her ethical responsibility to avoid putting someone at risk and will not violate federal law.

What If Mold or Water Damage Is Detected?

What if the agent or the inspector finds mold or conditions that are conducive to a mold infestation? For example, perhaps after the seller has moved out, the agent is doing one last walk-through of the house and discovers suspicious stains on a wall that had not been seen before because of the placement of furniture. Perhaps the seller knew nothing about it before the furniture was moved.

What next? First, the property owner should make sure the leak or water intrusion has been stopped. The buyer should request information that assures him or her that the seller has stopped the source of the water problem. If the leak or water infiltration continues, it might be wise for the buyer to find a more suitable home. Educate the buyer on his or her option to have the home tested.

In order to protect the buyer, the agent should get an extension of the Right to Terminate the Contract while the mold issues are being investigated. How to do this, of course, depends on specific state rules and regulations and the approved forms. And, yes, such an extension may cost extra money, delay closing, or even lose the sale. All of those are much preferable, however, to a Commission investigation, an unhappy buyer, or even a lawsuit. (By the way, most errors and omissions insurance policies do not cover mold—so here, the agent is "self-insured" and will probably have to pay any awards from a lawsuit himself or herself.)

If the seller convinces the buyer that the water problem has been corrected and if there is a mold problem associated with the water penetration, the seller may be able to clean up the mold in accordance with the methods summarized in Chapter 5.

When the agent checks off the inspections that the buyer wants, he or she should write in "mold" if this option is not specified on the contract. If the buyer doesn't want a mold inspection, write in or check off "not required." Any conversation(s) with the buyer in which he or she has stated that no mold inspection was necessary should be documented in case the buyer denies having made such statements later.

Testing for mold may be recommended for someone who has respiratory problems or who has been sensitized to mold or for families with infants or elderly members. The testing should be done in any areas that are suspected of harboring mold. In addition, because mold is everywhere, outdoor samples should also be taken and compared to the indoor samples: if the results of the indoor reading are similar to the outdoor reading, there may be no mold problem.

■ Locating a Professional "Mold Expert"

A reliable professional with experience and training in mold can often tell if mold or moisture testing is needed. How does one find such a professional "mold expert"? You may wish to consider:

- a **Council-certified Residential Mold Inspector (CRMI)**,
- a **Certified Industrial Hygienist (CIH)** with additional specialized microbial training,
- a Council-certified individual with microbial training, or
- another qualified person with experience with mold.

Whichever type of professional is hired, he or she should have documented experience with mold. Request references, and follow up with them for your own peace of mind.

Once you find a CRMI, a CIH, an environmental engineer, or other specialist, don't stop there. Get references. Make sure that he or she is qualified in indoor air quality and mold.

The CRMI designation is issued by the **American Indoor Air Quality Council (AmIAQC)** and follows the standards set by the **Indoor Environmental Standards Organization (IESO)**. The IESO has set strict standards for sampling (surface, air, and dust), and is an ANSI-standards setting body. **ANSI** is the acronym for the **American National Standards Institute**, which sets standards for nearly everything, from bottled water and packaged ice to drinking water additives and wastewater treatment units.

The CRMI must meet a number of requirements for the designation, including two years of documented experience, demonstrated proficiency with equipment, and the skills and knowledge required to interpret the results of tests. In addition, the CRMI must have attended at least a two-day review course on mold and passed a closed-book comprehensive examination.

The terms *industrial hygienist* and *indoor environmentalist* used alone are merely voluntary designations—they are not restricted by law. Therefore, anyone may call himself or herself an environmentalist or an industrial hygienist. There are certifications from the **American Board of Industrial Hygiene (ABIH)** for industrial hygienists (the Certified Industrial Hygienist, CIH), but most CIHs work in an industrial setting, and few are certified in mold.

Certifications are important. To protect yourself and to find someone who has demonstrated competence in the field, it is recommended that you use the services of a *certified* professional. These certification programs follow strict guidelines established by the **Council for Engineering and Scientific Specialty Board (CESB)**. The CESB is an independent, voluntary membership body created for its member organizations who recognize the expertise of individuals practicing in engineering and related fields through specialty certifications. To determine whether a specific certification is recognized by the CESB, visit their Web site at *www.cesb.org* and view the "Accredited Programs" link on the left side of the home page.

Many microbial and other indoor environmental professionals are certified by the American Indoor Air Quality Council. The AmIAQC accreditation programs are recognized by the CESB. To be certified by the AmIAQC, an individual must

- submit an application and provide documented project history to a certification board composed of experts who have field experience in the areas required for each certification,
- pass an intensive examination, and
- document the number of years of demonstrated experience pertinent to each certification being sought.

In addition, a Council-certified individual must keep up his or her certification through continuing education, practice, publications, teaching, etc., every two years.

Each member of the certification board must hold the certification that he or she votes to award. Board members develop and approve all examination materials and eligibility requirements, and they review all application materials. Approval for awarding certifications is given by unanimous vote.

There are approximately 5,300 active Council-certified individuals in the country. The easiest way to find one is to visit *http://iaqcouncil.org/locator/locator.htm*.

A professional with experience in the area of mold may be able to determine the amount of moisture in a ceiling or a wall without having to do major damage to the structure by using moisture meters and thermal imaging cameras that "see" through walls. These sophisticated cameras are not available at local hardware stores or big box retailers but must be purchased from professional specialty equipment providers such as Protimeter or FLIR Systems. FLIR Systems is the same company that provides thermal imaging devices to the U.S. military and also provides thermal imaging devices to indoor environmental professionals. Prices are high, though, with some equipment selling for as much as a new luxury car. Many professional indoor environmental consultants continually reinvest their profits into training and equipment.

Such a professional who is experienced in mold testing will also understand which tests will be most informative and which areas should be tested.

For Example

A large, black, slimy mass of mold was found growing on a windowsill in a home. The properly trained certified professional who came to do some sampling stated his belief that the results of air sampling would show little mold. He took samples from the mass of mold, and he took an air sample too. The results of the swab taken from the mold mass showed enormous amounts of mold. The air quality sample revealed only six spores, similar to the amount detected outdoors. The reason why the air quality sample was so low was that the spores had not yet been released from the mold mass, an event that could happen any time. Someone with less experience might mistakenly assume the absence of mold or of a potential mold problem from the results of that air sample.

■ What a Home Inspector Needs to Know

If a home inspector is interested in performing limited screen tests for mold, training to IESO standards for these tests is available. The home inspector can also be trained to provide the ERMI sampling protocol. These types of screen tests are cost-effective services that allows a buyer to determine if a high level of mold is present indoors. A home inspector who takes this training may then use these screen tests in conjunction with home inspections. The price of an ERMI or IESO screen is typically about the same as that of a home inspection, but it will vary by location. These screens can range in price from $400 to more than $1,000 depending on the size and/or remoteness of the home.

The home inspector should be watchful for signs of water damage, which are sometimes red flags suggesting the presence of mold. An inspector who neglects to identify water stains, negative drainage, dampness, or other indicators of water penetration during a home inspection may be considered negligent. If the buyer of the home becomes ill because of mold and if the inspector has not reported evidence of water leaks or penetration that had been detected in the home, the inspector might be found liable.

To protect against liability, an inspector must be aware of conditions that create an environment conducive to mold growth, such as

■ negative drainage;

■ leaking foundations or roofs;

■ damp or wet basements, crawl spaces, or attics;

■ leaky plumbing;

■ improper flashing that allows water to trickle inside walls;

■ improperly installed synthetic stucco; or

■ hail damage.

If synthetic stucco is detected, it might be wise to consult a moisture specialist.

An inspector should include a statement that he or she inspected only what was present and visible at the time of the inspection. The inspector's report may also indicate any areas that were inaccessible or to which there was limited access. An inspector cannot report what cannot be seen or smelled. Photographs included in the report are helpful.

Any adverse conditions observed during a home inspection should be reported. As much detail as possible should be provided in the report to protect against liability later.

■ What an Appraiser Needs to Know

In mold-related cases, the appraiser is at risk in much the same way as the home inspector is. Several claims have been made against appraisers in mold-related lawsuits. In each case, the plaintiff stated that the appraiser was negligent in failing to either discover or disclose a condition that allowed mold to develop for months or even years after the appraisal was performed.

How can an appraiser protect himself or herself against liability? By personally inspecting each property and bringing along a camera. If something looks like mold, the appraiser should take a picture of it, showing the extent of the mold on the date of the inspection. This information and the photograph should be included in the report. If the cause of the mold is not apparent, a statement to that effect should appear in the report. It might also be appropriate for the appraiser to indicate that he or she is not an expert in mold and therefore recommends an additional inspection by a qualified professional.

A waiver indicating that an appraiser inspects only visible and accessible areas is also recommended because mold may occupy areas that the appraiser cannot see. A home inspector may not be able to detect the mold either, because it may grow inside walls, above the ceiling, or under floors.

How will mold affect the value of a property? There are very few reports indicating the extent to which mold may decrease a property's value. Each appraiser should research his or her market for homes that had similar problems but were still sold.

■ What a Homebuilder or Remodeler Needs to Know

Homebuilders and remodelers should keep in mind that sometimes mold problems stem from faulty construction materials. During construction, building materials should be examined carefully, and any materials that are moldy should be discarded. If there is a rainstorm, building materials should be allowed to dry out completely before the building is enclosed; otherwise, moisture from the rain will be trapped inside and will provide a fertile breeding ground for molds. In building "green homes" with bales of straw, the bales should be allowed to dry out thoroughly before they are installed.

Regardless of the homebuilder's or remodeler's role in the sale of a property, the key to protecting oneself as much as possible is the same for everyone in the real estate industry: disclose, disclose, disclose. Unless the builder or remodeler—or anyone else working in the industry—actually *contributed* to the mold problem in some way, either directly or indirectly, the greatest liability to such a person in nearly any capacity results from failure to report a condition or fact that is known or suspected and then trying to disclaim knowledge of the information.

■ Chapter Seven Review Questions

1. An accurate and complete disclosure statement about water damage and mold isn't that important as it may actually lose the sale for you.

   a. True
   b. False

2. When listing a home, pay particular attention to signs of water damage in the home and do everything listed below *EXCEPT*

   a. use your nose to detect a musty smell, which may signify the presence of mold.
   b. watch for signs of water damage, such as blistering paint and peeling wallpaper.
   c. make sure the exhaust fans are working correctly and that the windows can be opened.
   d. rub a patch of mold to see how deeply it is growing.

3. A seller should be asked to provide a current CLUE report.

   a. True
   b. False

4. If there have been problems with water penetration and/or mold in the home, the agent or seller should do all the following *EXCEPT*

   a. disclose information about the water penetration and mold problems: when the problems occurred, what was done to fix them, and how quickly they were corrected.
   b. drop the listing right away.
   c. make sure that the seller fixed the source of the water problem.
   d. make sure that the seller replaced porous building materials infested with mold rather than painting over them.

5. Give the seller information about the CLUE database and how to order a CLUE report, and recommend that he or she order a CLUE report

   a. as soon as you obtain the listing.
   b. when you get a serious buyer looking at the house.
   c. after the buyer has submitted an offer.
   d. just before closing the sale.

6. If, during a final walk-through with a buyer after the seller has moved out, you find a stain on the wall that was not visible earlier, you should do all the following *EXCEPT*

   a. check the disclosure statement to see if a water infiltration event was reported that could have been responsible for the stain.
   b. contact the seller's agent or the seller and ask for more information.
   c. make sure that you have given the buyer information about mold.
   d. tell the buyer what you think he or she ought to do.

7. If you have an asthmatic buyer who is interested in a home that shows signs of mold, you should spend more time than usual with the buyer to make sure that he or she understands the potential problems with mold.

   a. True
   b. False

8. Instruct the buyer to obtain a CLUE report for the home by

   a. ordering it online or by phone.
   b. mailing a request to ChoicePoint.
   c. requesting it from the seller.
   d. requesting it from the National Association of REALTORS®.

9. Instruct the buyer to begin looking for homeowners' insurance

   a. a few days before the closing on the transaction.
   b. as early as possible in the transaction, preferably when the buyer begins to look for financing for the home.
   c. as soon as the buyer finds a home that he or she wants to buy.
   d. right after closing.

10. You should discuss mold with every one of your buyers and sellers, even if they don't seem interested.

    a. True
    b. False

Court Cases and Litigation

One of the reasons why public awareness of mold has increased so rapidly over the last few years is because of the many high awards paid in litigations resulting from problems related to "toxic mold." Due to the fact that many of these cases have resulted in multimillion dollar judgments, whereas others have involved high-profile individuals, these cases have been well publicized and have added enormously to public awareness of mold problems.

The literature is full of mold-related cases. A few of them are described here to give the reader an idea of the wide variety and scope of mold-related cases and the potential liability that a real estate professional can incur.

In addition, reviewing recent legal activities aids in the understanding of why mold has become such a hot issue, especially, perhaps, for those practicing law. It is commonly acknowledged in the mold-related literature that it all boils down to money—"mold is gold," according to some industry observers.

■ Examples of Some Mold-Related Stories

The Iler Family

According to an article published in *Time* magazine on July 2, 2001, Bruce and Sharyn Iler formerly lived in a home in Woodlands, Texas, which is an upscale suburb of Houston. Sharyn found that her eyes burned every time she went into the bathroom to put on her makeup. She suffered from other symptoms, as well: exhaustion, blurry vision, and a chronic dry cough. In February 2001, inspectors found mold between the stucco and the drywall of the Ilers' bathroom, master bedroom, study, and dining room. The Ilers were advised to evacuate their home; they took nothing with them but their dog and their cat.

The Porath Family

Many such stories involving mold—particularly "toxic mold"—have been reported by the media. For example, Steve and Karen Porath bought a repossessed home on a 5½-acre site in Foresthill, California, and they moved into it in April 1999. They began suffering health problems right away. Their son Mitchell was born two weeks later. Within two days, Mitchell curled up with stomach pains and vomited every day. His condition worsened: at one point, he was vomiting more than 50 times per day. No one could diagnose Mitchell's illness until the child was a year old, when a doctor suggested that molds or allergies might be the cause of the problem. The family had tests run, and mold was discovered. They were advised to vacate immediately and to leave all their possessions behind.

At that point, the Poraths had two options: they could spend $75,000 to fight the mold or have their home burned down. They estimated that they had already lost about $200,000 in building, testing, and medical costs and were deep in debt at this point. The house had been insured, but not against mold, so they had no insurance money. They chose the second option and had the local fire department burn their home, and all their possessions, to the ground on Valentine's Day in 2001.

In several other cases as well (for example, in Oregon and in Texas), families owned homes that were so heavily infested with mold that they were not worth the cost of corrective action and were burned down. In one such case, the family donated the home to the local fire department, which used the home for several training exercises before they burned it down.

■ Court Cases and Lawsuits Involving Mold in Residences

As indicated earlier in this book, many mold-related lawsuits have been filed beginning around the turn of the century. Some of these court cases have resulted in multi-million-dollar awards, which have fueled the growing hysteria about an organism that predates man and with which we have shared this planet peace-ably—until now. Many of these court cases were ostensibly breach of contract suits, but many others have been for property damage and personal injury because of a mold infestation. The bottom line for the court cases reviewed in this chapter, however, is that all these court cases revolve around mold.

Erin Brockovich v. Morrison Associates

Some of these cases have involved people with well-known names, such as Erin Brockovich, who bought a million-dollar home from the award she earned doing a report on the toxic chromium (VI) that was polluting the water supply of a small town in California. She is now having her home renovated to remove mold and has filed a suit over it (*Brockovich v. Morrison Associates*, No. 051037, Los Angeles Co. Super. Ct.).

Ed McMahon

Ed McMahon alleged that mold growing in his Beverly Hills mansion killed his dog and made his family sick. He sued his insurance company, two insurance adjusters, and several environmental cleanup contractors for $20 million because of their failure to fix a broken pipe that caused flooding and a subsequent mold infestation that was painted over rather than removed. (The case has been settled out of court for a total of more than $7 million.)

Most of those lawsuits have hurt the insurance companies, but a number of them have targeted real estate professionals.

Celmer v. Kotob

Several lawsuits have been directed against residential real estate licensees. For example, Melissa Celmer and her three boys moved into an apartment in Anaheim, California, in December 1995. They suffered no health problems for the first few years until water intrusion began to occur, which the owner of the apartment complex failed to fix. The water intrusion resulted in the growth of hidden mold in the apartment and the onset of health problems. The Celmers became so ill from the mold in their apartment that they had to move out of their home. They proceeded to sue everyone: the former owner of the apartment complex, the current owner, the property manager, and the remediation contractor (lawsuit filed in Superior Court in Orange County, *Celmer v. Kotob*, KDF North Hills, VPM Inc., and Rainbow Contractors). They settled for $900,000.

Stroot v. New Haverford Partnership

Elizabeth Stroot lived in an apartment in Wilmington, Delaware, for 21 months. Although she tried repeatedly to get her landlord to fix leaks in her bathroom, he failed to take action. Water leaked into her bathroom repeatedly. On May 16, 1994, the ceiling of her bathroom collapsed, and water from the ceiling flooded her bathroom, leaving drywall debris and the exposed ceiling covered with mold. Elizabeth had asthma, a condition that was exacerbated during the 21 months of residence in her apartment. During this period, Elizabeth had to go to the emergency room seven times because of severe asthmatic attacks, was hospitalized for nine days, and received steroids intravenously 12 times. She sued her landlord (*Stroot v. New Haverford Partnership*) and was awarded $1 million for personal injuries and $5,000 for property damage; the total was reduced by 22 percent (to a total of $818,390) for contributory negligence. The decision was upheld by the Delaware Supreme Court in May 2001 (*New Haverford Partnership v. Stroot*, 2001 Del. Lexis 201, May 7, 2001).

Mazza v. Raymond Schurtz

Then, there's the Mazza case. About six months after moving into the Partridge Point Apartments in Sacramento, California, all three members of the Mazza family became seriously ill—so ill, in fact, that they were repeatedly hospitalized and incurred nearly $125,000 in medical bills. They discovered that their illnesses had been caused by mold and requested that the Partridge Point Apartments complex reimburse them for their possessions that had been damaged by the mold and for their relocation expenses. They did not even request reimbursement of the medical bills. The apartment complex said "No." The Mazzas filed a personal injury suit against the Partridge Point Apartments. Even during the trial, the Mazzas tried to settle out of court. The apartment manager said "No." They should have settled— the verdict was for $2.7 million. The case was up for appeal, but the Sacramento Superior Court denied the defendants their motion for a new trial or judgment (*Darren Mazza et al. v. Raymond Schurtz et al.*, No. 00AS04795, Calif. Super., Sacramento, Calif.).

Not all the cases directly impacting the real estate industry have involved property managers. Real estate agents and brokers have been targeted as well.

Evans Family

In November 1995, Terrell and Candra Evans, of Las Vegas, Nevada, bought their very first home, an older resale. Less than two years later, in September 1997, they were forced to vacate the premises of their home because of the onset of a number of illnesses, including asthma in the children and chronic bronchitis in the adults. The reason for the illnesses was mold. Testing confirmed the presence of *Stachybotrys*, labeled by the media as the most notorious of the "toxic molds." The Evans family filed suit against their real estate agent and everybody else involved for insufficient disclosures, and the city has padlocked the Evans' home.

Richmond, Virginia

In Richmond, Virginia, a buyer moved into a home and began experiencing health problems. The heating and cooling contractor discovered mold in the duct system—mold that had been hidden by the seller's putting potpourri in the heating and cooling ducts to mask the musty smell of the mold! The buyer filed a complaint against the real estate licensee, who had acted as both the listing and the buyer's agent. No evidence was found that the licensee knew anything about the mold, and she was exonerated, although the decision *could* have gone the other way.

Structural Damage in California

In 1997, the new owners of a stilt home in California sued the sellers and their agents. The new homeowners sued because of the death of an adult son from the collapse of the house during an earthquake. The buyers claimed that the sellers and their broker had failed to disclose structural damage to the home that had been caused by mold. The case was settled for $2,150,000: $1,500,000 from the seller's real estate broker and agent and $650,000 from the sellers.

Komiyama v. City of Rialto

In another case in California, a family settled their lawsuit against the City of Rialto for $600,818 after a city contractor had caused raw sewage to back up into their home (*Komiyama v. City of Rialto*, 1997). The injuries alleged by the plaintiffs included brain damage and respiratory infections. Blood tests revealed that the family members had elevated levels of mold antibodies in their bloodstreams.

■ Court Cases and Lawsuits Involving Mold in Schools and Other Public and Commercial Buildings

Newspaper and online articles have appeared all over the country about schools and other public buildings that have had to be shut down and cleaned up because of health problems reported by people who spent time in those buildings. In some cases, class-action suits have resulted.

Andrejevic et al. v. Board of Education, Wheaton-Warrenville School District, Ill.

A class-action suit was filed in July 1999 seeking $67 million in damages (*Andrejevic et al. v. Board of Education of Wheaton-Warrenville School District No. 200*, DuPage County, Ill.). The suit was filed by about 1,700 students, parents, and teachers who alleged injuries caused by their exposure to "toxic mold" and other indoor air pollutants at an elementary school in Illinois. The mold in the school was caused by a flood that was not remediated properly.

Polk County Courthouse

Courthouses in Florida appear to be particularly susceptible to mold-related litigation. The Polk County Courthouse was built in 1987 for $37 million. "Toxic" mold was found, and the building was evacuated in 1992. By 1997, the total payout by the county because of the presence of the mold was $50.4 million including

- $33.7 million in building repairs,
- $10 million in defense expenses,
- $4.1 million in relocation costs, and
- $2.6 million for workers' health claims.

In addition, the county paid about $13.3 million in settlements. About 200 plaintiffs who had worked in the building filed a private party suit, which resulted in a verdict of $40 million, and third-party plaintiffs received about $8.9 million in out-of-court settlements from the general contractor, a number of subcontractors, and the design engineer.

Centex-Rooney Construction Co. v. Martin County

In a second case, a public owner sued a construction manager for breach of contract when mold was discovered in another new courthouse in Florida. The owner complained of excessive humidity and mold growth (*Aspergillus* and *Stachybotrys*) well into occupancy of the building, which was evacuated so that remedial action could be taken. The county filed suit against the builder, arguing that construction defects (the EIFS and a faulty heating, ventilation, and air conditioning system) were allowing water infiltration into the building, resulting in mold that was causing ailments in the courthouse employees. A jury awarded the county $11.5 million in damages plus $2.9 million in interest. The decision was upheld by a Florida appellate court in 1997 (*Centex-Rooney Construction Co. v. Martin County*).

Kristen M. Rhodes et al. v. BG Real Estate Services

In New Orleans, Louisiana, employees working in offices in the Plaza Tower filed a class-action suit, claiming exposure to mold that caused respiratory problems, headaches, and fatigue because of water leaks and unknown toxic substances that were making the employees ill (*Kristen M. Rhodes et al. v. BG Real Estate Services Inc. et al.*, No. 2001-18355, La Dist., Orleans Parish).

Christina E. Hughes v. Jorgensen Maintenance Services, Inc., et al.

An employee in Kentucky who worked for Toyota Motor Distributors, Christina Hughes, claimed that she was injured by exposure to mold (*Christina E. Hughes v. Jorgensen Maintenance Services Inc., et al.*, No. A0106410, Ohio Comm. Pls., Hamilton Co.). Her claims included negligence and gross negligence because Jorgensen Maintenance Services, retained by Toyota to maintain the buildings and mechanical systems at the facility, failed to perform their work in a workmanlike manner, resulting in Hughes' sustaining lost wages, medical expenses, pain, emotional distress, loss of enjoyment of life, and permanent and total disability.

■ Mold-Related Court Cases and Lawsuits Impacting the Homeowners' Insurance Industry

Although real estate licensees are very much at risk of being sued because of mold, it is the *insurance* industry that has been hit particularly hard by the increasing litigation involving mold, especially in Texas and California. Sometimes the insurance company has won, but often it is the consumer who has been on the winning side. Generally, the key factor to winning such a lawsuit is being able to connect the growth of mold to an insured loss, such as a sudden water leak.

Melinda Ballard Case

In one of the most publicized "mold cases" to date, Melinda Ballard and her husband Ron Allison and son Reece had bought a mega-million-dollar home in Dripping Springs near Austin, Texas. A leak developed, and mold set in. Again, the presence of *Stachybotrys* was confirmed. Ballard and her husband filed suit against their insurance company for not providing the money to clean up the leaks early enough. The jury awarded the family a whopping $32 million. However, in December 2002, the Third District Court of Appeals reduced the jury verdict against Farmers Insurance from $32 million to $4 million plus $2.5 million in interest and approximately $2 million in attorney fees. Ballard plans to appeal the decision. (Although the case is technically for breach of contract, it was based on a mold infestation.)

Chapter 1: Introduction: What Is Mold?

Margaret's newest clients, Ryan and Linda, have just found a white, leathery growth in their home. They always thought of mold as being black or greenish, so they have no idea what the growth in their home is, but they want to find out before they put their home on the market.

Margaret has another client, Dale, who is looking for a home. However, Dale's wife, Clara, is convinced that mold can be found only in filthy homes and that it is always harmful. So, even though Ryan and Linda's home sounds perfect for Dale and Clara, Margaret is hesitant to show it to them.

1. Margaret believes that white growth is a type of mold because she has read that mold doesn't have to be green or black but may be nearly any color. This is because

    a. mold always changes colors as it develops.

    b. there are many different species of mold, each with its own characteristics and colors.

    c. the mycelium of mold always starts out as white and leathery.

    d. all mold really is black or green.

2. Mold

    a. is always harmful.

    b. can never be cleaned up completely.

    c. should be destroyed wherever it appears.

    d. is necessary for life on Earth.

Student Comments

Please provide your comments regarding the basic principle(s) addressed in this case study and its relevance to the subject matter generally:

_____

_____

_____

_____

_____

case study	**Chapter 2: What Does Mold Look Like, How Does It Reproduce, and When Does It Thrive?**

Tammy has a client named Edna who is terrified of mold because of what she has heard and read about it. Her present home is too big for her since she is a widow and her children are grown up and have moved out, with families of their own. That is why Edna is looking for a smaller home. She is on a fixed income and has been looking for an older, well-established home. Tammy has found a lovely home for Edna, and Edna had a mold inspection performed on it. Only small quantities of mold spores were found, but Edna is still afraid of an infestation.

The seller of the home that Edna is considering told her that the water line to the icemaker in the refrigerator broke the day after the mold inspection was conducted. However, the problem was detected right away and was cleaned up within 24 hours.

1. Edna needs to understand that an infestation may occur in any home
   a. that is not kept cool and well lit.
   b. any time there is a food source present.
   c. any time there is moisture present where it doesn't belong (e.g., from a leak).
   d. only when the owner of a home intentionally brings mold spores into the home.

2. Because Edna is convinced that the water leak will lead to a mold infestation, she should
   a. be concerned because mold infestations may begin in less than 24 hours.
   b. not be concerned because it takes longer than 24 hours for an infestation to begin.
   c. have another inspection done.
   d. look for another home.

Student Comments

Please provide your comments regarding the basic principle(s) addressed in this case study and its relevance to the subject matter generally:

_____

_____

_____

_____

_____

Chapter 3: Why Has Mold Become a Problem?

Carol and Paul were ready to move out of their apartment and buy a home. They chose a brand-new home in a new housing development, found a loan for first-time homebuyers, and moved in. Within six months, however, they both began suffering from respiratory problems. They soon discovered that the bedroom carpet in front of the door to the bathroom was constantly damp and were shocked to find a large patch of a mold-like substance growing on the wall behind the desk. They called their contractor, who promptly ordered a mold inspection. Results from the inspection revealed an infestation due to a leaking pipe between the bedroom wall and the shower stall. Further investigation revealed that the pipe had been installed improperly.

1. The problem that Carol and Paul experienced
   a. is unique because mold problems usually do not flare up in new homes.
   b. is not unusual because new homes are typically built tightly, which minimizes the exchange of air between the outside and the interior of the home.
   c. was caused by the improper installation of the pipe behind the shower.
   d. Both b and c are correct.

2. Which of the following is *NOT* a factor in the increased number of reported problems with mold?
   a. Changes in weather patterns due to global warming
   b. Use of construction methods that make buildings tighter
   c. Increased media attention
   d. Leaving windows open in humid environments, which allows the exchange of air between the outside and indoors

Student Comments

Please provide your comments regarding the basic principle(s) addressed in this case study and its relevance to the subject matter generally:

_____

_____

_____

_____

| case study | **Chapter 4: Adverse Health Effects of Mold** |

A number of people working in the real estate industry have been sued over mold and "toxic mold" issues. These include real estate licensees, brokers, property managers, construction contractors, architects, appraisers, insurance companies, and others.

Jim has been a real estate licensee for 25 years. A year ago, he was the seller's agent in the sale of a lovely home. The home was purchased by Tim and his wife, Diane. About two weeks before closing, a hailstorm damaged part of the roof. The seller had the roof repaired and had the ceiling painted by a professional painter. Two months after the couple moved in, their three-month-old asthmatic daughter had to be hospitalized because of her exacerbated asthma attacks. Their two boys, ages two and three, developed allergic reactions and skin rashes at about the same time. Tim believed that "toxic mold" in the home was the culprit and seriously considered suing Jim and the seller.

1. Which statement is *FALSE?*
    a. Tim would probably *not* win his lawsuit because these are all classic symptoms induced by mycotoxins.
    b. There is no evidence of toxin production by mold as described here—these are all common symptoms that mold-sensitive individuals may experience.
    c. Babies and young children are particularly susceptible to mold because their immune systems are not yet fully developed.
    d. Symptoms often reported from exposure to "toxic molds" frequently include coughing up chunks of blood.

2. The most common illness observed from mold is
    a. aspergillosis.
    b. infections.
    c. asthma.
    d. allergic reactions.

Student Comments

Please provide your comments regarding the basic principle(s) addressed in this case study and its relevance to the subject matter generally:

_____

_____

_____

_____

_____

case study   **Chapter 5: Inspection and Remediation**

Stan and his wife Louise lived in a large home in the suburbs of a large city. All their children had grown up and moved out, so Stan and Louise decided to buy a smaller home that would be easier to take care of. They contacted Barbara, a licensee who specializes in listings. When they were walking through the home together, Barbara noticed a patch of mold in the bathroom. She mentioned it and told Stan and Louise that they would need to clean it up before showing the home. Stan and Louise asked her how to clean it up.

1. What should Barbara *NOT* do?
   a. Give Stan and Louise a copy of the EPA brochure about mold
   b. Tell Stan and Louise how to clean up the mold in the bathroom and suggest that they hire someone to clean it up for them if someone in their family shows signs of having respiratory problems
   c. Give Louise and Stan information about how to clean up various sizes of mold infestations or refer them to the appropriate Web sites
   d. Give Stan and Louise information about health effects of mold or refer them to the appropriate Web sites

2. Which of the following are *NOT* needed to clean up most small mold infestations (10 square feet or less)?
   a. Goggles
   b. Rubber gloves
   c. An N-95 respirator
   d. A self-contained breathing apparatus

Student Comments

Please provide your comments regarding the basic principle(s) addressed in this case study and its relevance to the subject matter generally:

_____

_____

_____

_____

Glen has been a real estate agent and broker for many years. He has a successful business and an excellent reputation in his home state of California. Glen deals primarily with residential property but also works with commercial property at times.

Glen listed one residential property in which a mold infestation developed because of leakage through a roof that was damaged when a tree fell on it. The seller not only replaced the roof; he also had the attic, walls, and ceiling near the area where the roof was damaged inspected for mold and had all infested building materials replaced. A final mold test revealed that the number of spores was no higher inside the home than outside.

1. Did Glen offer the seller good advice when he told him *NOT* to disclose the previous infestation because it was cleaned up successfully as determined by testing?

    a. Yes, because California law does not require disclosure of mold in a residence that was cleaned up properly.

    b. Yes, because California law requires disclosure after remediation for commercial properties only.

    c. No, because California law requires full disclosure of past or present mold, regardless of whether remediation was successful or not.

    d. No, because California law requires disclosure if the size of the infestation was greater than 30 square feet.

Recently, Glen listed a commercial property with a minor mold problem, in which mold was found on about 20 square feet of ceiling tile because of a small leak in the roof. Again, the seller had remediation done, and PCR analysis revealed low concentrations of Group II molds and no significant levels of Group I molds.

2. Did Glen offer the seller good advice when he told the seller *NOT* to disclose the previous infestation because PCR analysis indicated that remediation had been successful?

    a. Yes, because California law does not require disclosure of mold in a commercial building that was cleaned up properly.

    b. No, because the California bill requires disclosure of all mold-related events for all properties.

    c. No, because California law requires full disclosure of past or present mold for commercial properties, whether or not remediation was successful.

    d. Yes, because California law requires disclosure only if the infestation in a commercial property was greater than 30 square feet in size.

One of Glen's friends, Pat, is also a real estate agent in California. Pat has just obtained a listing for a home with a mold problem, but no remediation has been done because the seller doesn't believe the problem to be serious. Glen advised Pat to include a disclosure about the mold, but Pat feels that this is not sound advice because no permissible standards have been set for mold.

3. By *NOT* disclosing the mold problem, Pat made the right choice.

    a. True

    b. False

Student Comments

Please provide your comments regarding the basic principle(s) addressed in this case study and its relevance to the subject matter generally:

_____

_____

_____

_____

Chapter 7: Reducing Liability

Jan is listing a home owned by John and Sally. When she walked through the house, she noticed a few signs of water damage. Having taken a class on mold, she realized that there may be some problems associated with the water damage. She informed John and Sally of the potential problems and gave them a copy of the EPA's brochure on mold, provided information from the EPA and the CDC Web sites, and stressed the importance of full disclosure of all potential problems, particularly relating to the water damage. Though Jan did not see or smell any evidence of mold, she warned them that a potential buyer might want to have a mold inspection done before deciding to buy the home. Jan asked them if they had filed any insurance claims on the house, to which John and Sally replied that they had filed a claim for hail damage about eight years ago. Jan provided them with the information they needed to order a CLUE report and suggested they order one right away.

Don and his family of five are very interested in John and Sally's home. While walking through the home, Laura, one of Don's children, shows signs of acute respiratory problems and makes frequent use of an inhaler. Don's agent expresses concern over Laura's condition and proceeds to give them a great deal of information about mold and "toxic mold," telling Don that he usually doesn't spend this much time covering mold but is concerned about Laura. He then suggests that the Don put a humidifier in Laura's room. He also recommends that they request a CLUE report from John and Sally and that they also request a mold test.

1. What did Jan do wrong?
    a. Jan should not have requested that the John and Sally order a CLUE report until they had a potential buyer lined up.
    b. Jan should have told them that their claim for hail damage would show up on their CLUE report.
    c. Jan should have asked them about the water damage and should have made sure that the water leak had been fixed.
    d. Jan should have dropped the listing as soon as she discovered signs of water damage.

2. What did Don's agent do right?
    a. He made recommendations about placing a humidifier in Laura's room.
    b. He suggested that Don's family request a CLUE report from John and Sally.
    c. He suggested that Don request a mold test.
    d. Both b and c are correct.

Student Comments

Please provide your comments regarding the basic principle(s) addressed in this case study and its relevance to the subject matter generally:

_____

_____

_____

Acremonium strictum a mold commonly found in low concentrations in homes throughout the United States. An ERMI Group II mold.

AHHS American Healthy Home Survey, conducted by the EPA and HUD.

allergen a material in the environment that can cause an allergic reaction in certain individuals; examples are pollen, animal dander, viruses, bacteria, and mold

allergy an immune reaction to a small amount of material in the environment after a person has been exposed to that material and has been sensitized to it

Alternaria alternata a mold commonly found in low concentrations in homes throughout the United States. An ERMI Group II mold.

American Board of Industrial Hygiene (ABIH) the not-for-profit corporation that sets the standards for Certified Industrial Hygienists. ABIH certifications are CESB-accredited.

American Indoor Air Quality Council (AmIAQC) the not-for-profit organization that maintains and verifies all credentials for council-certified indoor environmental quality professionals. AmIAQC certifications are CESB-accredited.

American National Standards Institute (ANSI) standards the organization that develops standards for many products in the United States.

antibiotic a drug that fights diseases caused by microorganisms such as bacteria, viruses, or mold

antibody a type of protein produced by white blood cells to protect the body from antigens by neutralizing these foreign particles

antigen a small, foreign material, such as a mold spore or fragment of mycelium, a bacterium, or a pollen grain, that causes the formation of antibodies by the immune system to protect the body

ARMI the acronym for American Relative Moldiness Index, a modified ranking system for determining the relative moldiness of a home based on the analysis of 13 different molds: 3 from Group II and 10 from Group I. This index is not used nearly as frequently as the ERMI.

aspergillosis an infection caused by certain species of *Aspergillus*, particularly *Aspergillus flavus*, *Aspergillus fumigatus,* and *Aspergillus niger*

Aspergillus a genus of household mold with species from both ERMI Groups I and II; some species produce mycotoxins or cause infections under certain conditions

Aspergillus flavus a mold often found in high concentrations in water-damaged homes throughout the United States. An ERMI Group I mold. This species sometimes invades tissues of immunocompromised individuals as a parasite.

Aspergillus fumigatus a mold often found in high concentrations in water-damaged homes throughout the United States. An ERMI Group I mold. This species sometimes invades tissues of immunocompromised individuals as a parasite.

Aspergillus niger a mold often found in high concentrations in water-damaged homes throughout the United States. An ERMI Group I mold. This species sometimes invades tissues of immunocompromised individuals as a parasite.

Aspergillus ochraceus a mold often found in high concentrations in water-damaged homes throughout the United States. An ERMI Group I mold.

Aspergillus penicillioides a mold often found in high concentrations in water-damaged homes throughout the United States. An ERMI Group I mold.

Aspergillus restrictus a mold often found in high concentrations in water-damaged homes throughout the United States. An ERMI Group I mold.

Aspergillus sclerotiorum a mold often found in high concentrations in water-damaged homes throughout the United States. An ERMI Group I mold.

Aspergillus sydowii a mold often found in high concentrations in water-damaged homes throughout the United States. An ERMI Group I mold.

Aspergillus unguis a mold often found in high concentrations in water-damaged homes throughout the United States. An ERMI Group I mold.

Aspergillus ustus a mold commonly found in low concentrations in homes throughout the United States. An ERMI Group II mold.

Aspergillus versicolor a mold often found in high concentrations in water-damaged homes throughout the United States. An ERMI Group I mold.

Aureobasidium pullulans a mold often found in high concentrations in water-damaged homes throughout the United States. An ERMI Group I mold.

average surface temperature the average temperature over the land masses of the earth; a parameter sometimes used to estimate the extent of global warming

biofilm a fine layer of a biological growth, such as mold, growing upon a thin film of substrate, such as wallpaper, wallpaper paste, dust, or water-based paint containing cellulose

biomarker a chemical in the body that indicates whether an individual has been exposed to a particular disease-causing organism or condition; none are known that indicate the presence of mold

cellulose the type of starch found in wood, ceiling tile, etc.; the primary food source of household molds

Certified Industrial Hygienist (CIH) a professional who has been certified by the American Board of Industrial Hygienists (ABIH) to be dedicated to the health and well-being of humans. A CIH may now specialize in the area of indoor environmental quality (IEQ)

Chaetomium globosum a mold often found in high concentrations in water-damaged homes throughout the United States. An ERMI Group I mold.

chronic bronchitis one of the two most common forms of obstructive lung disease

chronic lung disease long-term respiratory problems; includes asthma, emphysema, and chronic bronchitis

Cladosporium a genus that includes several household molds; two species are often found in low concentrations in "normal" homes (ERMI, Group II), and one may be found in higher concentrations in water-damaged homes (ERMI, Group I)

Cladosporium cladosporioides, var. 1 a mold commonly found in low concentrations in homes throughout the United States. An ERMI Group II mold.

Cladosporium cladosporioides, var. 2 a mold commonly found in low concentrations in homes throughout the United States. An ERMI Group II mold.

Cladosporium herbarum a mold commonly found in low concentrations in homes throughout the United States. An ERMI Group II mold.

Cladosporium sphaerospermum a mold often found in high concentrations in water-damaged homes throughout the United States. An ERMI Group I mold.

colonization the growth, ripening, and distribution of a new batch of spores

Comprehensive Loss Underwriters Exchange (CLUE) a database used by insurance companies to determine whether or not to cover a homebuyer; also, a report that a homeowner can obtain, based on information in the database, that provides information about any claims filed for a property within the last five years. CLUE reports can be ordered from ChoicePoint at *www.choicetrust.com* for about $9 by phone or for about $12 to $15 online.

conidia spores produced by many species of mold at the end or along the sides of a conidiophore

Council-certified Residential Mold Inspector (CRMI) an individual who has taken a two-day class, has passed an exam on mold inspections, has documented experience, and uses the IESO standards for sampling and mold inspections

Council of Engineering and Scientific Specialty Boards (CESB) the recognized accreditation body for engineering and scientific certification and specialty certification programs

digestion the process of breaking down large molecules into small ones that can be used by the body; used by animals and fungi

digestive enzymes proteins that facilitate the digestive process in animals and fungi

DOHMH New York City's Department of Health and Mental Hygiene—responsible for promulgating guidelines for cleaning up mold, from small areas to large infestations

dormant inactive, like spores before they are activated by the conditions they need to germinate

emphysema one of the two major types of obstructive lung disease

Epicoccum nigrum a mold commonly found in low concentrations in homes throughout the United States. An ERMI Group II mold.

ERMI the acronym for Environmental Relative Moldiness Index, a modified ranking system for determining the relative moldiness of a home based on the analysis of 36 different molds, 10 from Group II and 26 from Group I

Eurotium amstelodami a mold often found in high concentrations in water-damaged homes throughout the United States. An ERMI Group I mold.

external digestion the digestive process used by fungi, in which digestive enzymes are secreted into the food source through the hyphae and break down the cellulose into sugars; the sugars thus released from cellulose are then absorbed through the hyphae, back into the mold's mycelium and used by the mold for growth

exterior insulation & finish system (EIFS) artificial stucco

false negatives test results suggesting the absence of something (e.g., mold) when it actually is present

false positives test results indicating that a material (e.g., mold) is present when it actually is not

fungus (plural: fungi) a group of organisms such as mushrooms, puffballs, molds, and rusts or smuts that feed by external digestion, absorbing nutrients from the surrounding area

Fusarium a common household mold, but not one included in the ERMI ranking system

global warming increases in the surface air temperature induced by the greenhouse effect, which is caused by the emission of greenhouse gases into the air

glucan a constituent of fungal cell walls that has immunosuppressive and inflammatory properties

greenhouse gases gases contributing to global warming, such as carbon dioxide, methane, nitrous oxide, and fluorocarbons

Group I molds molds commonly found in high concentrations throughout the United States; they are considered to indicate water damage in a home. There are 26 Group I molds for the ERMI.

Group II molds molds commonly found in low concentrations throughout the United States that are considered to be indicators of a "normal" moldiness rating as defined by the ERMI. There are ten such species listed for the ERMI.

health standards standards that require the adoption or use of one or more practices to ensure healthful employment and places of employment. See also *standards (health or safety)*.

hemorrhage bleeding

HUD the Department of Housing and Urban Development, which has been trying to ameliorate some of the mold-related problems in the housing industry

HVAC systems heating, ventilation, and air conditioning systems

hypersensitive a condition of increased sensitivity to an antigen such as mold, usually caused by repeated exposure to the antigen

hypersensitivity pneumonitis inflammation of the lungs

hyphae the branched, tubular filamentous strands that make up the mycelium of the mold

IESO (Indoor Environmental Standards Organization) a nonprofit organization that certifies individuals who have taken their two-day class, have passed their exam, and subscribe to the IESO standards of practice for sampling and performing mold inspections

immune system the body's defense mechanism against foreign materials such as bacteria and molds

infection invasive growth of a parasite into a person's body tissue

internal digestion the process of digestion in animals, in which food is digested within the body, primarily in the stomach and small intestine; the small molecules resulting are then dispersed to the rest of the body through the bloodstream

invasive aspergillosis the condition that occurs when an infection in the lungs caused by certain species of *Aspergillus* spreads to other systems or organs of the body, such as the brain, the heart, the kidneys, or the liver. Virtually any organ or system in the body can be infected.

irritation soreness and redness of the skin or mucous membranes; sometimes caused by exposure to the volatile organic compounds (VOCs) produced by molds

kingdom classification of each of the five major life forms (animal, plant, fungus, Protista, and Monera) based primarily on the cellular structure of the organisms and on the constituent organisms' relationship to food

Melina Bill a bill introduced into the House of Representatives in 2002 by Rep. John Conyers, Jr. This proposed bill, named the U.S. Toxic Mold Safety and Protection Act of 2002, is often referred to as the Melina Bill after the daughter of one of Rep. Conyers's staff members, who allegedly lost 70 percent of her lung function because of mold.

mold a group of filamentous fungi that live on either (1) living plants or animals, (2) organic nonliving material, or (3) dead plants/animals or their waste. These fungi secrete enzymes that break down the material in which they thrive and absorb the broken-down products as food. Molds in the second group are considered here.

mold-specific quantitative polymerase chain reaction (MSQPCR) a test for mold based on DNA analysis that can be used to determine the relative moldiness of a building.

Mucor amphibiorum a mold commonly found in low concentrations in homes throughout the United States. An ERMI Group II mold.

mycelium (plural: mycelia) a mass consisting of the hyphal structures of the mold; the "body" of the mold

mycotoxin a toxic chemical produced by a mold

obstructive lung disease   a lung disease such as emphysema or chronic bronchitis that causes a narrowing or obstruction of the airways in the lungs

opportunistic pathogen   an organism that can cause disease in an individual with a pre-existing condition that makes it possible for the opportunistic pathogen to cause the disease

PD&R   HUD's Office of Policy Development and Research, which has sponsored several projects focusing on building practices and technologies to help prevent moisture (and mold) problems.

Paecilomyces variotii   a mold often found in high concentrations in water-damaged homes throughout the United States. An ERMI Group I mold.

parasite   an organism that lives on a living plant or animal host

PATH Program   the Partnership for Advancing Technology in Housing Program sponsored by HUD's Office of Policy Development and Research (PD&R)

pathogen   a disease-causing organism or material

PDF   portable document format; a file type that is readable with free software from Adobe

Penicillium   a genus of mold with many species, one of which is commonly found in low concentrations in homes throughout the United States and is an ERMI Group II mold. A number of *Penicillium* species are found in high concentrations in water-damaged homes throughout the United States (ERMI Group I mold). Penicillin, a mycotoxin, was derived from one of the species of *Penicillium* mold.

Penicillium brevicompactum   a mold often found in high concentrations in water-damaged homes throughout the United States. An ERMI Group I mold.

Penicillium chrysogenum   a mold commonly found in low concentrations in homes throughout the United States. An ERMI Group II mold.

Penicillium corylophilum   a mold often found in high concentrations in water-damaged homes throughout the United States. An ERMI Group I mold.

Penicillium crustosum   a mold often found in high concentrations in water-damaged homes throughout the United States. An ERMI Group I mold.

Penicillium purpurogenum   a mold often found in high concentrations in water-damaged homes throughout the United States. An ERMI Group I mold.

Penicillium spinulosum   a mold often found in high concentrations in water-damaged homes throughout the United States. An ERMI Group I mold.

Penicillium variabile   a mold often found in high concentrations in water-damaged homes throughout the United States. An ERMI Group I mold.

photosynthesis   the process in which plants convert simple molecules (water and carbon dioxide) to sugar, which is then converted to more complex molecules in the form of starch (primarily cellulose)

pneumonia   an inflammation of the lungs that may be caused by bacteria, viruses, or a fungal infection

polymerase chain reaction (PCR)   a relatively new test based on DNA analysis

pulmonary   pertaining to the lung

pulmonary hemorrhage   bleeding from the lungs; a condition observed in several infants in Cleveland that caused a number of deaths in which *Stachybotrys* and smoking were implicated

quantitative polymerase chain reaction (QPCR)   a test based on DNA analysis

remediation   to clean up or fix; to restore

reversible (disease)   a disease or condition that can be reversed, at least in part, so that the patient improves. For example, some illnesses caused by mold can be reversed if the sick person is removed from the mold source. The disease may not be reversible if too much damage has been done.

Rhizopus stolonifer   a mold commonly found in low concentrations in homes throughout the United States. An ERMI Group II mold; commonly referred to as bread mold.

safety standards   standards that require the adoption or use of one or more practices to ensure safe employment and places of employment. See also *standards (health or safety)*.

saprophyte   an organism that lives on dead or non-living organic material

scientific name   the two-part name of a species. The first letter of the first name is capitalized and represents the group of related species, or genus (i.e., it is generic); the second part is not capitalized and is the species name (i.e., it is specific).

Scopulariopsis brevicaulis   a mold often found in high concentrations in water-damaged homes throughout the United States. An ERMI Group I mold.

Scopulariopsis chartarum   a mold often found in high concentrations in water-damaged homes throughout the United States. An ERMI Group I mold.

sensitization   single or repeated exposure to an allergen that results in the individual's becoming hypersensitive to that allergen

sinusitis   an inflammation of the membranes of the nose and the sinus cavity. This inflammation of the sinuses can result from an immune response to the fungi: the immune system sends specialized white blood cells (eosinophils) to attack the fungi, and the eosinophils irritate the membranes in the nose and sinuses.

species   a type of organism with common characteristics; members of the same species can usually interbreed.

sporangium (plural: sporangia)   spore case in which spores are formed

spores   microscopic one-celled structures produced by molds to propagate themselves; they are very resistant to usual methods of cleaning while dormant

Stachybotrys   the type of mold generally implicated in "toxic mold" problems; although there are 17 known species of *Stachybotrys*, only *Stachybotrys chartarum* (or *Stachybotrys atra*) is known to produce mycotoxins under certain conditions

standards (health or safety)   acceptable limits of a hazardous material that have been set by an agency to protect health and safety

starches   large, complex molecules composed of sugars; the starch cellulose is the main constituent of plant tissues

substrate   the material (food) upon which household molds feed

sugars   small molecules that make up starches, such as the cellulose found in plant tissues; digestion breaks down the starches into their component sugars, which can then be used as food

test kits   inexpensive kits for testing molds, which are generally inaccurate and may lead to false positives or false negatives

threshold limit values (TLVs)   certain types of health standards which are generally used as guidelines for determining the level of protection needed to protect an individual from a particular hazardous material

toxic   poisonous; repeated exposure may lead to illness or even death

"toxic" mold   the molds that release poisonous materials (or "mycotoxins"); does not include those species of molds that merely trigger allergic or asthmatic reactions, infections, or irritations

Trichoderma viride   a mold often found in high concentrations in water-damaged homes throughout the United States. An ERMI Group I mold.

volatile organic compounds (VOCs)   organic compounds released by molds that produce the distinctive musty odor commonly associated with molds. Many VOCs are solvents, and some are toxic, especially to sensitive people or those with respiratory problems. VOCs from molds are known to cause irritations in sensitive individuals.

Wallemia sebi   a mold often found in high concentrations in water-damaged homes throughout the United States. An ERMI Group I mold.

Mold-Related Legislation and Information from Federal Agencies and Congress

Centers for Disease Control and Prevention (CDC)

Information about mold, mold cleanup, and health effects is available at *www.cdc.gov/mold*.

Facts about mold and dampness are at *www.cdc.gov/mold/dampness_facts.htm*.

U.S. Department of Housing and Urban Development (HUD)

For information about mold, remediation, health issues, and more, go to the "Healthy Homes" section of the HUD Web site, *www.hud.gov/offices/lead/healthyhomes/mold.cfm*.

U.S. Environmental Protection Agency (EPA)

The EPA's informative site at *www.epa.gov/mold* includes many links at *www.epa.gov/iaq/molds/index.html*.

The EPA publication *A Brief Guide to Mold, Moisture, and Your Home*, EPA 402-K-02-003, is available at *www.epa.gov/mold/pdfs/moldguide.pdf*.

For information on ordering the EPA's Indoor Air Quality Tools for Schools (IAQ TfS) Action Kit, EPA 402-K-05-001 (hard copy) or 402-C-05-001 (CD-ROM), go to *www.epa.gov/iaq/schools/actionkit.html*. Most of the action kit can be downloaded in PDF or Word format from the site as well.

The EPA publication *Mold Remediation in Schools and Commercial Buildings*, EPA 402-K-01-001, can be found at *www.epa.gov/mold/pdfs/moldremediation.pdf*.

Guidance for Clinicians on the Recognition and Management of Health Effects Related to Mold Exposure and Moisture Indoors, published by the Center for Indoor Environments and Health with support from a grant by the EPA, can be downloaded at *http://oehc.uchc.edu/CIEH.asp*.

U.S. House of Representatives

Information about the proposed legislation for the United States Toxic Mold Safety and Protection Act (the Melina Bill) introduced by Rep. John Conyers, Jr., in 2002, including the full text of the legislation, is at *www.house.gov/conyers/mold.htm*.

Mold-Related Legislation and Information from State and City Agencies

Arizona Department of Real Estate

For helpful articles, go to *www.azre.gov* and search for the keyword *mold*.

New York City Department of Health and Mental Hygiene

One of the earliest sources of information about mold, with some excellent material, particularly about remediation of mold, is the DOHMH's *Guidelines on Assessment and Remediation of Fungi in Indoor Environments*. Go to *www.nyc.gov/html/doh/html/epi/moldrpt1.shtml*.

Articles and Online Newsletters about Mold

National Association of REALTORS® (NAR)

Available to all readers is Jill Freudenwald's "Mold in the Home: How It Affects REALTORS®" at *www.realtor.org/gapublic.nsf/pages/moldpapers*.

Also available to the public is Anne-Marie Siudzinski's "Field Guide to Mold & Health Issues" at *www.realtor.org/libweb.nsf/pages/fg711*.

Available to REALTORS® only is the *Report of the Mold Working Group of the Risk Management Committee* at *www.realtor.org/letterlw.nsf/pages/0502mold*.

Inman News Features

Inman News Features offers both free and paid subscription services at *www.inman.com*. The paid subscription service is necessary to access articles that are more than four days old.

Realty Times

Realty Times offers a free subscription service at *http://realtytimes.com/agentnews.htm*.

The IEQ Review

Pure Air Controls from the *IEQ Review*, *www.imakenews.com/pureaircontrols*, is a weekly newsletter with some very good articles about mold.

Toxic Mold and Tort News Online

Toxic Mold and Tort News Online provides information on litigation and links to several helpful sites related to molds at *www.toxic-mold-news.com*.

ABIH® and Industrial Hygiene. *www2.abih.org/query/ABIH_roster.asp.*

Acme Environmental. *www.acmeenvironmental.com.*

American Board of Industrial Hygiene. Certified Industrial Hygienist (CIH)—what it means. *www.abih.org/Docs/what-is-cih.htm.*

American College of Occupational and Environmental Medicine. Adverse Human Health Effects Associated with Molds in the Indoor Environment. 2002. *www.acoem.org/guidelines.aspx?id=850.*

Ammann, Harriet M., PhD. Is Indoor Mold Contamination a Threat to Health? *www.doh.wa.gov/ehp/oehas/mold.html.*

Arizona Department of Health Services. Indoor Air Quality Info Sheet: Mold in My Home: What Do I Do? *www.hs.state.az.us/edc/ehpage.html.*

Ashley, Peter, Dr., John R. Menkedick, and Maureen A. Wooton. *Healthy Homes Issues: Mold.* U.S. Department of Housing and Urban Development, External Review Draft, Version 2. October 2, 2001.

Borenstein, Seth. Ocean warming tied to stronger hurricanes. The Boston Globe. *www.boston.com/news/nation/washington/articles/2008/01/31/ocean_warming_tied_to_stronger_hurricanes/.*

Bowdoin, Michael. How Many Ways Can Mold Impact Real Estate Professionals? *Indoor Air Currents,* August/September 2002, Vol. 3, Issue 1, *www.eletra.com/baq1/e_article000095515.cfm.*

Brandt, Mary, et al. Mold Prevention Strategies and Possible Health Effects in the Aftermath of Hurricanes and Major Floods. *CDC MMWR,* Recommendations and Reports, June 9, 2006, *www.cdc.gov/mmwr/preview/mmwrhtml/rr5508a1.htm.*

Buettner, Mike. Respircare Analytical. Personal communication with author (see also *www.RespirCareAnalytical.com*).

Building Science Corporation. Mold on their minds: home builders grapple with moisture matters. February 11, 2002. *www.Inman.com/hstory.asp?ID=28406&CatType=R.*

California's Toxic Mold Protection Act of 2001. *www.leginfo.ca.gov/pub/bill/sen/sb_0701-0750/sb_732_bill_ 2001.1007_chaptered.html.*

Centers for Disease Control and Prevention (CDC). Molds in the Environment. *www.cdc.gov/nceh/asthma/factsheets/molds/moldfacts.htm.*

Centers for Disease Control and Prevention (CDC). Questions and Answers on *Stachybotrys chartarum* and other molds. *www.cdc.gov/nceh/asthma/factsheets/molds.*

Charlesworth, David. Acme Environmental Co., Albuquerque, NM. Personal communication. (See alsp *www.acmeenvironmental.com.*)

Chew, Ginger L., Jonathan Wilson, Felicia A. Rabito, Faye Grimsley, Shahed Iqbal, Tilna Reponen, Michael L. Mullenberg, Peter S. Thorne, Dorr G. Dearborn, and Rebecca L. Morley. 2006. Mold and Endotoxin Levels in the Aftermath of Hurricane Katrina: a Pilot Project of Homes in New Orleans Undergoing Renovation, *Environmental Health Perspectives* 114(12), 1883–1889.

CLUE® Personal Property. ChoicePoint. *www.choicepoint.net/industry/insurance/pc_ins_up_2.html.*

Commentary on Legal Issues. *MoldUpdate.* National Association of Mutual Insurance Companies. *www.moldupdate.com/litigation.htm.*

Committee on Damp Indoor Spaces and Health, Board on Health Promotion and Disease Prevention, Institute of Medicine of the National Academy. Damp Indoor Spaces and Health. *www.nap.edu/openbook.php?isbn=0309091934.*

Committee on Environmental Health, American Academy of Pediatrics. 1998. Policy Statement: Toxic Effects of Indoor Molds (RE9736), *Pediatrics 101*, no. 4: 712–714, *www.aap.org/policy/re9736.html.*

Congressman John Conyers, Jr. Introduces H.R. 1268: The United States Toxic Mold Safety and Protection Act (the Melina Bill). *www.house.gov/conyers/mold.htm.*

Consumer Affairs. Insurance Rates Up Sharply in Katrina's Wake. consumeraffairs. com. *www.consumeraffairs.com/news04/2006/02/katrina_premiums.html* (February 1, 2006).

Consumer Affairs. Judge Rules Against State Farm in Katrina Case. consumeraffairs.com. *www.consumeraffairs.com/news04/2007/01/katrina_state_farm.html* (January 11, 2007).

Consumer Affairs. Mold Sickens Hurricane Survivors…and Mortgage Lenders. consumeraffairs.com. *www.consumeraffairs.com/news04/2005/katrina_mold.html* (October 5, 2005).

Dearborn, Dorr G., Paul G. Smith, and Terrence M. Allan. Pulmonary Hemorrhage and Hemosiderosis in Infants, Case Western Reserve University, *http://gcrc.cwru.edu.stachy.*

DeRosa, Jerry V. 2006. Mold Assessment and Management. Occupational Health and Safety, May 2006. *www.ohsonline.com/articles/44997.*

Effects of global warming. Wikipedia. *http://en.wikipedia.org/wiki/Effects_of_global_warming.*

Eilperin, Juliet. World Temperatures Keep Rising with a Hot 2005. washingtonpost.com. *www.washingtonpost.com/wp-dyn/content/article/2005/10/12/AR2005101202498.html.*

Elidemir, Okan, Giuseppe N. Colasurdo, Susan N. Rossmann, and Leland L. Fan. 1999. Isolation of *Stachybotrys* from the Lung of a Child with Pulmonary Hemosiderosis. *Pediatrics* 104(4): 964-966, 4 October 1999, *http://pediatrics.aappublications.org/cgi/content/abstract/104/4-964.*

Elphinstone, J. W. 2008. U.S. Court Cites Mold Study, Indicates Reversal in Lawsuits. *Commercial Property News*, February 4, 2008. *www.cpnonline.com/cpn/property_type/article_display.jsp?vnu_content_id=1000671832.*

EMLab P&K. *www.emlabpk.com.*

EMSL, ERMI and ARMI Sampling Guide. *www.emsl.com/PDFDocuments/Sampling Guide/EMSL%20ERMI%20ARMI%20Sampling%20Guide.pdf.*

Engel, Brett. Acme Environmental Co., Albuquerque, NM. Personal communications and photographs. (See also *www.acmeenvironmental.com.*)

Environmental Health Investigations Branch, California Department of Health Services. Health Effects of Toxin-Producing Indoor Molds in California. *www.dhs.cahwnet.gov/org/ps/deodc/ehib/EHIB2/topics/toxin_producing.html.*

Environmental Protection Agency (EPA). *A Brief Guide to Mold, Moisture, and Your Home. www.epa.gov/iaq/molds/moldguide.html.*

Environmental Protection Agency (EPA). *Aspergillus niger* Final Risk Assessment. *www.epa.gov/opptintr/biotech/pubs.fra/fra006.htm.*

Environmental Protection Agency (EPA). Global Warming—Climate. *www.epa.gov/oar/globalwarming.nsf/content/climate.html.*

Environmental Protection Agency (EPA). Global Warming—Emissions. *www.epa.gov/oar/globalwarming.nsf/content/emissions.html.*

Environmental Protection Agency (EPA). Mold Remediation in Schools and Commercial Buildings, EPA 402-K-01-001, March 2001. *www.epa.gov/iaq/molds.*

Environmental Protection Agency (EPA). Mold Resources. *www.epa-gov/iaq/pubs/moldresources.html.*

Environmental Protection Agency (EPA). Molds & Moisture. *www.epa.gov/iaq/molds/index.html.*

Evans, Blanche. 2002. CLUE Reports: The Next Sellers' Disclosure. *Realty Times*, August 5, 2002. *http://realtytimes.com/rtnews/rtapages/20020805_cluereports.htm.*

Finigan, Rich. 2001. What You Should Know about Mold. *Communicator*, Winter 2001, *www.frea.com/frea/mold.htm.*

Freudenwald, Jill, Mold in the Home: How It Affects Realtors®, *www.realtor.org/gapublic.nsf/pages/moldpapers.*

FSEC. Managing Mold in Your Florida Home: A Consumer Guide. Florida Solar Energy Center (FSEC). *http://fsec.ucf.edu/bldg/mold.*

Fungal Sinusitis. *Mold-Survivor. www.mold-survivor.com /fungal_sinusitis1.htm.*

General Re Corporation. Hazardous Times: Toxic Mold. *GeneralCologne Re*, October 2000.

Gots, Ronald E., MD, PhD. Correcting Mold Misinformation. *www.wmmic.com/ infodocs/mold.htm.*

Hamilton, Anita. Beware: Toxic Mold. *Time*, July 2, 2001. *www.odatus.net/mold/time/ index.html.*

Hamilton, Bruce. Insurers hit with flood of Katrina lawsuits. *The Times-Picayune*, September 12, 2006. *www.nola.com/archives/t-p/index.ssf?base/library-111/1158041325 69180.xml&coll=1.*

Harman, Patricia L. 2001. Mold Remediation 101: An Overview. *Claims*, December 2001: 29–31.

Hartwig, Robert P., PhD. 2002. Mold and Insurance: Truth and Consequences. PowerPoint presentation from August 2002, accessed from *www.iii.org/media/ hottopics/insurance/mold2.*

Household Mold, Consumer Information and Education Forum for Home Owners. Study Finds High Mold Levels in Post-Katrina New Orleans Air. *http://mold .openflows.org/study-finds-high-mold-levels-in-post-katrina-new-orleans-air* (June 15, 2006).

Huffman, Mark. Mississippi Sues State Farm over Katrina Coverage. consumeraffairs.com. *www.consumeraffairs.com/news04/2007/06/ms_state_farm.html* (June 11, 2007).

Hurricane Insurance Information Center. Fact File: The Mold Problem and Insurance Coverage. *www.iii.org/disaster2/facts/mold.*

IEQ Review. Toxic Mold Bill Reintroduced, *The IEQ Review*, April 9, 2003, *www.imakenews.com/eletra/mod_print_view.cfm?this_id=141327.cfm?xa1BgICF,aV80Lic.*

Indoor Environmental Standards Organization. *www.iestandards.com/certtrain .index.asp.*

Institute of Medicine of the National Academies. 2004. Damp Indoor Spaces and Health. *www.nap.edu/openbook.php?isbn=0309091934.*

Insurance Claims Services. ChoicePoint. *www.choicepoint.com.*

Jacob, Beate, et al. 2002. Indoor Exposure to Molds and Allergic Sensitization. *Environmental Health Perspectives*, 110, no. 7. July 2002.

Jacob, Jany K. Construction Faces New Foe: Toxic Mold. Seattle Daily Journal of Commerce. *www.agcwa.com/public/newsletter/2001/oct/toxic_mold.asp* (October 2001).

Kirby, Alex. Warming climate "means worse weather." BBC News. *http://news.bbc .co.uk/1/hi/sci/tech/946739.stm* (September 28, 2000).

LexisNexis Mealey Publications. Mealey's Litigation Report: Mold, December 2001 (Volume 1, Issue #12), *www.mealeys.com/mold.html*.

Liability Insurance Administrators. Mold: the Hidden Menace. *www.liability.com/menace.html*.

Lillard, Susan. Court of opinion amid suits over mold. Mold-Help.org. *www.mold-help.org/content/view/748/*.

Lin, King-Teh. Benefits of Applying Moldiness Index Abound. *www.mycometrics.com/articles/ERMI_Lin_IEC2007.html*.

Lind, K. Michelle. FAQs about Mold. *www.aaronline.com/docs/mold_faq.asp*.

Macher, Janet (ed.). 1999. *Bioaerosols: Assessment and Control*. Cincinnati: American Conference of Governmental Industrial Hygienists (ACGIH).

McClusky, O. Edwin, MD. 2002. Black Mold and Human Illness. Texas Medical Association Council on Scientific Affairs, *SCA Report* 1-1-02. September 2002.

McCrady, Ellen. 1999. Mold: The Whole Picture, Pt. 1, *Abbey Newsletter* 23, no. 4 1999. *http://palimpsest.stanford.edu/byorg/abbey/an/an23/an23-4/an23-402.html*.

McNeel, Sandra V. and Richard A. Kreutzer. 1996. Fungi & Indoor Air Quality. *Health & Environment Digest* 10, no. 2 May/June 1996: 9-12. *www.dhs.cahwnet.gov/org/ps/deodc/ehib/EHIB2/topics/fungi_indoor.html*.

Minnesota Department of Health. Mold in Homes. *www.health.state.mn.us/divs/eh/indoorair/mold/index.html*.

Mold Working Group of the Risk Management Committee of National Association of REALTORS®. Report of the Mold Working Group of the Risk Management Committee. National Association of REALTORS®. *www.realtor.org/letterlw.nsf/pages/0502mold* (April 2002).

NAHB Research Center, Inc. 2002. *Durability by Design*. Washington, DC: HUD USER. *http://www.huduser.org/publications/destech/durdesign.html*.

National Association of REALTORS®. Louisiana Home Builders Face Tougher Rules. *Daily Real Estate News*, December 28, 2005.

National Association of REALTORS®. State Association Assessments of Scope of Problem and Legislative Responses: Insurance Survey of State REALTOR® Organizations. *www.realtor.org/GAPublic.nsf/Pages/insurvey?OpenDocument*.

New York City Department of Health and Mental Hygiene Guidelines on Assessment and Remediation of Fungi in Indoor Environments. *www.ci.nyc.ny.us/html/doh/html/epi/moldrpt1.html*.

New York City Department of Health and Mental Hygiene. Facts about Mold. *www.ci.nyc.ny.us/html/doh/html/epi/epimold.html*.

Newport Partners LLC. 2006. Moisture-Resistant Homes: A Best Practice Guide and Plan Review Tool for Builders and Designers with a Supplemental Guide for Homeowners. Department of Housing and Urban Development Office of Policy Development and Research.

O'Hollaren, M.T., et al. Exposure to an Aeroallergen as a Possible Precipitating Factor in Respiratory Arrest in Young Patients with Asthma. The New England Journal of Medicine, reprinted in The IEQ Review, April 15, 2003.

Opdyke, Jeff D., and Christopher Oster. 2002. Is Your House Uninsurable? *Wall Street Journal*, May 23, 2002.

Pinto, Michael A. An Overview of *Stachybotrys* Mold. *www.wondermakers.com/an_overview_of_stachybotrys.htm*.

Pure Air Control Services, Inc. 2003. Court Cases Involving Damages Due to Mold, Mold Update. *The IEQ Review. www.imakenews.com/pureaircontrols/e_article 000127084.cfm*.

Pure Air Control Services, Inc. Mold-Related Legislation Introduced in Six States So Far This Year. *The IEQ Review*, February 26, 2003, *www.imakenews.com/pureaircontrols/e_article000129810.cfm*.

Realty Times. 2001. REALTORS® Can Help Prevent Mold Suits. *Realty Times*, June 4, 2001.

RespirCare Analytical *www.RespirCareAnalytical.com*.

Riggs, Russell W. 2002. Mold: NAR Helping Its Members Manage Their Risk. National Association of REALTORS® *Real Estate Outlook*, May 2002: 12–13.

Romano, Jay. Managing Mold, and Lawsuits. *The IEQ Review. www.imakenews.com/pureaircontrols/e_article000132290.cfm* (March 5, 2003).

Ruel, Tim. 2002. Problems with Mold Not New in Waikiki. *Honolulu Star-Bulletin Hawaii News. http://starbulletin.com/2002/07/26/news/story3.html* (July 26, 2002).

Salvant, Lucien. Property Insurance Fact Sheet. National Association of REALTORS®. *www.realtor.org/Public Affairs Web.nsf/Pages/InsFactSheet?OpenDocument*.

Salvatore, Steve. Fungus Causes Most Chronic Sinusitis, Researchers Say. CNN. com. *www.cnn.com/HEALTH/9909/09/sinusitis*.

Schindler, Eric J. Toxic Mold Litigation: A Plaintiff's View. 12th Annual Conference of the California Industrial Hygiene Council, December 9–11, 2002. *http://artoflaw. lawoffice.com/article5pdf.pdf*.

Schoppa, Jack C. Mold, Moisture, Stigma and Value. *Appraiser e-Gram*, October 2002. *www.naifa.com/gram/2002oct/schoppa-oct02.html*.

Schoppa, Jack C. Will Sudden, Accidental Events Be Covered If Mold Is a Danger? *Realty Times. http://realtytimes.com/rtnews/rtapages/20020903_mold.htm* (September 3, 2002).

Schubert, Belinda. 2001. Toxic Mold. *Real Estate Business Outline*, September/October 2001, *www.crs.com/members/magazine/reb205/infocus.html*.

Siudzinski, Anne-Marie, Field Guide to Mold & Health Issues. *www.realtor.org/libweb.nsf/pages/fg711*.

Star-Telegram. 2002. Timeline of a Crisis. Star-Telegram, Dallas/Fort Worth, October 21.

Storey, Eileen, and Kenneth H. Dangman, Paula Schenck, Robert L. DeBernardo, Chin S. Yang, Anne Bracker, and Michael J. Hodgson. Guidance for Clinicians on the Recognition and Management of Health Effects Related to Mold Exposure and Moisture Indoors. *http://oehc.uchc.edu/clinser/MOLD%20GUIDE.pdf*.

Sudakin, Daniel L., MD, MPH. 2002. *Stachybotrys chartarum*: Current Knowledge of Its Role in Disease. *The IEQ Review. www.imakenews.com/pureaircontrols/e_article 000070030.cfm* (May 8, 2002).

Texas Department of Insurance. Effectively Handling Water Damage and Mold Claims: A Consumer Guide. *www.tdi.state.tx.us/consumer/moldpub.html* (April 2002).

Texas Office of the Attorney General. What Consumers Should Know about Mold. *www.oag.state.tx.us/consumer/mold_remed.shtml*.

University of Minnesota, Department of Environmental Health & Safety, Indoor Fungi Resources. Fungal Glossary. *www.dehs.umn.edu/iaq/fungus/glossary.html*.

www.pathnet.org/sp.asp?id=18574.

Yost, Nathan, Frequently Asked Questions about Mold. *www.realtor.org/realtororg. nsf/pages/moldfaq/OpenDocument*.

Yost, Nathan. Health Effects of Exposure to Mold: Review of the Scientific Literature: 1990–2002. *www.realtor.org/gapublic.nsf/pages/moldhealth*.

Chapter 1

1. b
2. b
3. b
4. d
5. d
6. c
7. c
8. a
9. b
10. b

Chapter 2

1. b
2. d
3. c
4. d
5. b
6. c
7. a
8. c
9. a
10. d

Chapter 3

1. a
2. b
3. d
4. b
5. d
6. a
7. b
8. b
9. b
10. b

Chapter 4

1. b
2. d
3. d
4. a
5. b
6. c
7. b
8. b
9. d
10. b

Chapter 5

1. b
2. d
3. c
4. b
5. b
6. b
7. b
8. a
9. c
10. a

Chapter 6

1. a
2. c
3. c
4. a
5. a
6. b
7. b
8. d
9. a
10. b

Chapter 7

1. b
2. d
3. a
4. b
5. a
6. d
7. b
8. c
9. b
10. a

■ Case Studies

Chapter 1

1. b
2. d

Basic principles: Mold may be found everywhere and is necessary for life on earth. There are many different species of mold, and each species has its own characteristics, including color.

Chapter 2

1. c
2. b

Basic principles: Mold requires the presence of moisture in order to germinate and colonize. A food source is also required, but food sources are virtually everywhere in most homes. A mold infestation can form quickly, but mold spores require at least 24 to 48 hours to begin colonizing; other species may require more time. Therefore, if moisture is cleaned up right away, there should be no chance of an infestation unless the leak has not been fixed.

Chapter 3

1. d
2. d

Basic principles: New homes are just as prone to mold infestations as older ones because of the tighter construction methods generally used. In addition, poor design, construction defects, improper installation of materials, and defective materials may add to the potential for mold infestations. Other factors that may contribute to the increased attention to mold problems are changes in weather patterns because of global warming, reporting by the media, and the large number of lawsuits, including some with very large sums of money that have been awarded to plaintiffs.

Chapter 4

1. a
2. d

Basic principles: The most common reaction to common household mold is some form of allergic reaction. In more sensitive individuals, asthmatic symptoms may be exacerbated. These symptoms can develop in any susceptible individual from virtually any type of common mold—they are not caused specifically by "toxic molds." Indeed, the mycotoxins produced by some molds under certain conditions may cause more severe symptoms, but this has not been substantiated scientifically, and such mycotoxin-induced health effects have become much more difficult to prove in court.

Chapter 5

1. b
2. d

Basic principles: A real estate agent should not represent himself or herself as an expert on mold or on a client's medical condition. Instead, the agent should give the client the information (e.g., the EPA brochure, applicable fact sheets, and the addresses of informative Web sites such as the EPA, the CDC, and NAR sites) so the client can make his or her own decisions on cleaning up the mold in the home.

A self-contained breathing apparatus is not generally needed for cleaning up a small mold infestation—an N-95 respirator suffices.

Chapter 6

1. a
2. a
3. b

Basic principles: Both the California Toxic Mold Act and the proposed Melina Bill require disclosure. However, the California act does not require disclosure of mold (in either a residential or a commercial building) if the mold has been successfully cleaned up. (This is not true of the proposed Melina Bill.) Disclosure of mold that has not been remediated is strongly recommended to protect both the seller and his or her real estate agent, even though no permissible limits have been set.

Chapter 7

1. c
2. d

Basic principles: The real estate agent should have asked about the signs of water damage and should make sure that any problem with water intrusion has been fixed. She should emphasize to the seller that disclosure is vital, particularly if there has been any water damage and/or mold infestations in the home. The agent should recommend that the seller request a CLUE report right away to ensure there are no claims appearing that might make it difficult for a buyer to purchase homeowners' insurance on the home. The agent should take care not to represent himself or herself as an expert on mold or on health conditions that can result from mold and an individual's sensitivity to it. However, the agent should give his or her client information about mold (e.g., the EPA brochure and the addresses of reliable Web sites that address mold, such as the EPA, CDC, and NAR). The agent should not make statements that could incorrectly imply that he or she has a medical background. Also, the agent should spend no more time with someone who may be particularly susceptible to mold than with anyone else because that could put him or her in potential violation of the Fair Housing Act.